We '

Almost by accident, in 1951, David Childs went as a teenager to The 'Third World Festival of Youth and Students' in Communist East Berlin. This was the start of a life-long interest in Germany. Over the decades, he met many leading German personalities including General Wolf Graf von Baudissin, Heinrich Böll, Rainer Eppelmann, Stefan Heym, Egon Krenz, Hans Modrow, Hans Joachim Schädlich, Helmut Schmidt, General Hans Speidel, Stephen Thomas, Walter Ulbricht and Herbert Wehner. He met very many others, unknown warriors or victims of the Cold War. As his files later revealed, he was himself spied upon, in Britain as well as in Germany, by the Stasi, over a long period.

Emeritus Professor David Childs has contributed many books on German and British history including The Fall Of The GDR (2001) and the ever popular Britain Since 1945 (2006). He continues to write and speak on both countries.

Also By David Childs

Among the other books by David Childs are:

The Fall Of The GDR
The Two Red Flags
The Stasi
Germany In The 20th Century
The GDR Moscow's German Ally
Britain Since 1945: A Political History - Sixth Edition
Britain Since 1939 - Progress And Decline

http://www.davidchilds.co.uk/

We Were No Heroes

David Childs

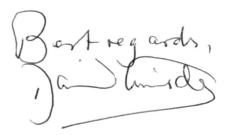

Grange BS

Published by Grange BS 2009

David wishes to thank

Martin Childs for his contributions, and both Martin and Julian Childs for their editorial work, Dr Kay Blumenthal-Barby, Roger and Cenzi Loewig, Peter Johnson, formerly Reuter's correspondent Moscow and East Berlin, and the BStU (Bundesbeauftragte für die Unterlagen des Staatssicherheitsdienstes der ehemaligen Deutschen Demokratischen Republik) - Office of the Federal Commissioner Preserving the Records of the Ministry for State Security of the former GDR.

The author alone is responsible for the contents of this book.

Abbreviations:

BND - Bundesnachrichtendienst (West German Federal Intelligence Service)
DDR - Deutsche Demokratische Republik (East Germany)
DEFA - Deutsche Film-Aktiengesellschaft (GDR State-owned film company)
DGP - Deutsche Grenzpolizei (German Frontier Police)
DVP - Deutsche Volkspolizei (East German People's Police)
FDJ - Freie Deutsche Jugend (Free German Youth)
FDP - Freie Demokratische Partei (Free Democratic Party)
KGB - Komitet Gosudarstvennoy Bezopasnosti (National Security Agency of the USSR)
HVA - Hauptverwaltung Aufklärung (Main Administration Reconnaissance, Stasi's Foreign Intelligence Department)
NSDAP - Nationalsozialistische Deutsche Arbeiterpartei (National Socialist German Workers' Party - Nazis)
NKFD - Nationalkomitee Freies Deutschland (National Committee for a Free Germany)
NVA - Nationale Volksarmee, (National People's Army, East German armed forces)
SED - Sozialistische Einheitspartei Deutschlands (Socialist Unity Party of Germany; East German Communist Party)
SPD - Sozialdemokratische Partei Deutschlands (Social Democratic Party of Germany)
SS - Schutzstaffel (Protective Squadron, Nazi Elite Guard)
Stasi - Staatssicherheit or State Security, short for Staatssicherheitsdienst, State Security Service
Waffen SS - Armed SS, the military wing of the SS

Prologue

This attempt at an autobiography only became possible after the collapse of the German Democratic Republic whose officer I was. Even though my Waffen-SS service was known to my employers in the Stasi, my British origins were not and it would not have been possible for me to reveal the well-kept secret of those origins. As far as British laws are concerned, I now realise that it is doubtful that much would have happened to me had I fallen into British hands still wearing the uniform of the Waffen-SS in 1945. A considerable number of Britons were investigated after 1945 for their services to the Third Reich. In most cases no action was taken, the notable exceptions being John Amery and William Joyce who were in due course sentenced to death and executed. In some other cases short prison sentences were handed down. It is only recently that I read about this by-way of British history.

Why bother writing an autobiography at all? I am aware that all autobiographies are self-justification on the part of those who write them. But I have tried to be as honest as I can. I am writing first and foremost for my son, Heinrich, a generous, liberal, 'liberated' and fair-minded individual whom I have neglected because of the demands of my work. I hope he will be better able to understand his father, and his father's generation, by reading it. Should I be lucky enough to find a publisher, I hope the book will provide a wide audience with some understanding of the dilemmas individuals like me were faced with and why we sometimes made the wrong choices.

Although the totalitarian regimes of the 20th century have been defeated or collapsed from their own internal contradictions, it is the nature of the human condition that future generations will also be faced with similar dilemmas.

Martin Thomas

1.

Childhood on Guernsey: those beautiful flying machines

Even with the post-Freudian advances in psychiatry it is still impossible to be sure why one man becomes a serial killer and another a successful brain surgeon, one a saint and another a sinner. Is it Destiny? Is it in your stars? Is it the accident of place and time? Is it hereditary? Is it your place in the family or the early childhood environment? Who can say? I know that in my case, as an only child in the 1930s, the 'pictures', illustrated magazines, old books and the 'wireless' greatly influenced me, as did an absent father and the fact that we moved home several times in my early years.

My mother greatly enjoyed going to the pictures and took me to *The Palace* or *The Regal* once a week. To her credit, it must be said that she liked more serious films, though we saw our fair share of comedy too, George Formby and Laurel and Hardy among them. But the films that stood out were David Niven and Errol Flynn as doomed flyers in *Dawn Patrol* and Gary Cooper and Franchot Tone as daring British officers in *Lives of a Bengal Lancer*. I also remember I was a Spy with Madeleine Carroll playing a World War I Belgian nurse-turned-spy opposite Conrad Veidt as the sophisticated German officer. I loved war movies. Germans like Veidt came across as interesting foes - although they appeared no match for our brave boys! You could admire them, unlike many of the 'natives' in the great British Empire epics like Alexander Korda's *The Four Feathers*. The whole atmosphere on Jersey and Guernsey, where I spent my childhood from age two, conspired to make you love the Army, the King and the Empire and be suspicious of 'natives' and other foreigners.

Another influence was aviation. I had lived near planes and airfields all of my early years; first in England, then in Jersey and finally in Guernsey. I loved watching the planes taking off and landing, mainly those elegant DH89, De Havilland Dragon Rapide biplanes. How wonderful they looked on a fine summer's day with their tapered wings, purring twin engines located in well-streamlined nacelles and slim yet roomy cockpits. They carried just eight passengers. For me, however, they carried much more. They carried all the promise, romance, glamour and adventure of foreign parts, which for us included the mainland of England as well as nearby France and distant cities – Berlin, Brussels, Cairo, Rome, Shanghai, Stockholm and Vienna among them. My mostly absent father was connected with aviation. As a birthday treat when I was 11, I was taken up in a DH89 on my first ever flight. It was magical. I remember feeling a little anxious, but once in the air the sensation was unbelievable. It was truly amazing looking out of the small windows at the tiny houses and boats and even smaller people; I remember thinking how they reminded me of an ant colony as they rushed about. We cruised at about 150mph out to sea and back again. Getting off the plane afterwards I felt 'grown up'. At school I became a bit of a celebrity and was everyone's friend for a time. My father was a flyer who had been employed by various airlines and was killed in an accident in Spain in 1938 working for General Franco. As I later discovered, he was not a 'warrior'; he had been engaged as a civilian, flying anything and everything. But he was, nevertheless, a heroic figure in my eyes. Because of my father, Spain and its civil war were, for me, full of romance, drama and tragedy. Later I was to think of him flying General Franco to his date with destiny in a DH89, but of course, although the *Caudillo* did indeed fly in a British DH89 in 1936, it was not with my father as pilot.

My father's death, when I was just 12, made little practical difference to my life. I continued at my grammar school, continued my reading of history books borrowed from the local library, continued to play with my soldiers, continued to watch the planes and continued to go to the pictures with my mum. Mother continued with her job as a part-time secretary to a local businessman. I do not know whether my father left her any money or pension, but she seemed to earn enough to keep us in modest prosperity.

To me, she was an attractive slender, dark-haired, brown-eyed woman and I think men found her so too. In her family she had been teased as 'the gypsy princess', but her looks were part of her Anglo-Irish inheritance. Three men called after my father's death. The first was the mysterious 'Mr Julio' who, at this distance of time and memory, appeared to come about three times. He told me to be proud of my father and gave me a box of Spanish soldiers. I know he gave my mother photographs, documents and some money. In one of the photographs he appeared in Spain with my father next to a plane I was never able to identify, both clad in leather flying jackets. He had all the dash and gallantry one associated with Spanish officers. Slender, even gaunt, he wore a stylish Douglas-Fairbanks moustache and a double-breasted suit and smoked heavily. The smell of his 'foreign' tobacco, though not unpleasant, lingered for days after his departure. The second visitor was a tall, blond, blue-eyed, rather sad-looking German. He too appeared to give my mother money and he gave me a model aircraft, which I later recognised was a Junkers 52 transporter. I always called him 'Frankenstein' and mother never corrected me. This must have been the influence of the film *Frankenstein* with Boris Karloff and the fact that we were not used to German names. We probably only knew Frankenstein, Göring, Schmidt and, of course, Hitler.

Our final caller, mother's employer Mr Spencer, called from time to time, usually with a little gift for me, which automatically endeared him to me (at that fickle age). The first was a set of cigarette cards of British Empire soldiers, which he must have collected from cigarette packets over several weeks. Looking back, he must have been a prolific smoker! I also learned that he must have been well-to-do as he smoked Players, which were regarded as quite upmarket. He obviously liked my mother but I don't think she seriously contemplated re-marrying. I tingled with embarrassment once when I 'caught' Mr Spencer kissing mother goodnight as he was leaving. Subconsciously, I must have regarded him as no match for Ronald Coleman, Gary Cooper, Errol Flynn, David Niven, Conrad Veidt or indeed, 'Mr Julio'. He probably fantasised a great deal as he had few outlets from the world of business. Once I came in and found a book, with plain covers, open on the settee. 'He longed for her as he had never longed for a woman before. Beneath the shimmering folds of her dress he seemed to see her naked body: her firm young breasts allured him.' Before I could read much more, a flustered Mr Spencer hastily picked up the book without comment.

He was always filling my head with tales of past wars and his part, real or imaginary, in them. He had been a prisoner-of-war in Germany and I believe he delighted in seeing me squirm when he recalled how they had been forced to eat roast rat when the Red Cross parcels failed to arrive. He also filled me with blood curdling stories about the Bolsheviks and their outrages in Russia. Although we never talked about party politics, I suppose I always assumed that he, and we, were for the British 'National' government of Neville Chamberlain. Mr Spencer was a *Daily Mail* reader and my mother used to bring it home after he had read it. She read mainly items directed at women, whilst I enthused over accounts of wars in China, Abyssinia, Spain and elsewhere. The *Daily Mail* supported Franco and was for appeasement of Nazi Germany and Fascist Italy. Mr Spencer agreed with the paper's owner, Lord Rothermere, that although Herr Hitler was a bit of a rough diamond, he, as a former front-line soldier, certainly did not want another war. He was delighted when he saw a picture of the Duke of Windsor and his American bride visiting Hitler. 'I always knew he should have remained King,' he commented. Others must have agreed with him because when the Duke appeared in newsreels he was more likely to be applauded than his brother George VI.

My childhood development was speeded up by the 'wireless'. It seemed quite fantastic that you could simply turn a knob and listen to London and hear the garbled noises from places farther afield such as Berlin, Paris and Rome plus many other more exotic destinations. There was also the music. What a wealth of classical music was made available to those of us who would not have the opportunity to visit a concert hall! The music of our English composers, the three knights, Arthur Bliss, William Walton and Edward Elgar thrilled me from the first moment I heard them. I did not have to be told what I ought to like. The BBC offered so many foreign composers as well, too many to mention. However, Manuel de Falla's music haunted me more than most, perhaps because of my father's involvement in Spain. It was thrilling to be sitting at home and listening to a live concert from the Royal Albert Hall.

Without doubt, one of the most electrifying radio experiences was hearing the abdication of King Edward VIII in 1936 and another was Neville Chamberlain explaining to us on 3rd September, 1939 that we were at war with Germany and that we were fighting 'evil things'. After that nothing much seemed to happen. There were more parades by the TA militia and Mr Spencer complained about the sudden increase in income tax and 'dark forces' that were behind the war. He, like most people, was shocked by the rapid advance of the Germans in Poland, claiming however, 'I always said that's how it would be if they started.' Life seemed to carry on as normal. The tourists continued to come, school continued and so did the weekly visits to the cinema. 'Was this really what war was like?' I recall thinking, 'it's not like that at the pictures.'

Christmas 1939 was better than ever. Mr Spencer came laden with presents among which was a fine Dinky set of a British anti-aircraft artillery unit for me and French perfume and a blouse for mother. Much later, I realised he must have stopped over, for he was with us for two days. Meanwhile, there was another war - the 'Winter War' between the Soviets and the Finns. Mr Spencer and I were wholeheartedly for the Finns and were depressed when they were forced to compromise with Stalin. I was excited to see the newsreel at The Regal showing the German pocket battleship *Graf Spee* in flames. Mr Spencer went on about how the gallant Captain Langsdorf (Hans) had gone down with his ship after ordering his crew ashore. This, however, turned out not to be the case; he shot himself in his Montevideo hotel room.

At school there was a thinning out of the male staff as they went off to war. Nothing else changed much. It was a Church of England institution where the philosophy of education seemed to be 'spare the rod, spoil the child'. Two strokes could be expected for arriving late, unauthorised talking, copying the work of others, allowing others to copy your work, lack of cleanliness and many other offences. Miss Norris taught with cane in hand most of the time. She hammered home the multiplication tables with it, the capitals of the distant parts of the British Empire with it, and the Ten Commandments with it. It never seemed to leave her side. I guessed she even ate and slept with it close to hand. Miss Norris was plump rather than fat, wore glasses and was immaculately turned out in a conservative sort of way. She nearly always wore a brown tweed suit and her hair in a bun. Everything about her appearance nonetheless was fresh and polished. She smiled rarely and seemed very contented with her lot. She always had a distinctive scent about her, which, though not my favourite, was not unpleasant and it helped mask the other pungent smells in the classroom. Years later, I realised that it was lavender. The war was not really discussed except that we prayed for victory and assumed that God was on the side of King George VI and his armed forces. We celebrated Empire Day at our, and, no doubt, every other school. It was a bit of fun dressing up if you got the right part. The only part I remember having was that of an Australian sheep shearer.

I was probably from a slightly superior social background than the average child at the school. I lived in a 'border' area between a proper middle class suburb, on the one hand, and a working class area on the other. There were a few shopkeepers' children in the class and even a solicitor's son, but most children came from still more humble backgrounds. For some reason, my mother knew Miss Norris slightly and that afforded me some protection. One thing they had in common was that they were both *Daily Mail* readers. I know this because I saw a copy of the paper on Miss Norris's desk from time to time. I would think, though I am not absolutely sure, that this fact enhanced the paper's prestige in my eyes. My mother had another thing in common with Miss Norris, in that they were both alone. It was said that Miss Norris had lost her fiancé in the First World War. Whether this was said just to win sympathy for her, give her additional prestige, and make her appear more normal or to strengthen the view that everyone had a partner of the opposite sex, I do not know. It was true that she was of the generation of women who had found it more difficult to find a husband because of the previous war's colossal losses.

1940 looked as though it was going to be like any other year we had known. There was a bad winter but the promise of a good summer. The prospects for the tourist trade appeared bright, as mainlanders wanted to get away from the gloom of wartime England. I remember my mother looking at tourist advertisements in the London papers describing the islands as 'the safest place on earth' as she considered taking tourists. The reason for this was probably Mr Spencer. Suddenly he was gone. I never got a proper explanation for his disappearance. 'It's the war you know, he had to go to England to do his bit,' was all I got from my mother. I never did understand or find out exactly what business he did, but I always imagined it to be something important. I soon realised that I missed him and his stories. I even missed his catch phrase, 'It won't be long now.' I never did quite find out what he meant by that. Although he cut no heroic figure, with his sagging frame covered in a three-piece pin-striped business suit, he was always lively, happy and considerate. He was kind to my mother, made me laugh, taught me chess, brought me presents and, above all, fired my imagination. His presence and the smell of his cigars seemed to make our modest semi-detached house grander, more palatial. Now it seemed empty and altogether smaller. We no longer indulged in the dinners with the table laid as for a special occasion, with the best crockery and linen napkins. His disappearance seemed to be the harbinger of far greater changes, the end of old certainties and the beginning of a new stage in our lives.

2.

Life under occupation

With Mr Spencer gone we no longer got immediate interpretations of the latest news and rumours. However, I followed the war from the radio and used a map to plot developments. I was shocked when in May 1940, my German markers moved first through Norway and Denmark, and then, Luxembourg. Holland and Belgium fell like dominoes to the swift thrusts of Hitler's Blitzkrieg. My German markers seemed to sprout up everywhere and at an alarming rate. Certainly, in the case of Holland and Belgium we had been led to believe they would put up strong resistance. Holland was supposed to have impregnable water defences and Belgium impregnable forts. In addition, much was made, in our media, of France's Maginot Line, reported to be the greatest system of impregnable fortifications ever built. The pace of the German advance was breathtaking. In Britain, Chamberlain fell and Churchill took over. What did it all mean? Were we next on Hitler's list? No one seemed to know.

We noticed some obstacles were erected at Guernsey airport only to be dismantled later. The few RAF and other British personnel seem to disappear without any announcement. On 19 June, the evening paper, *The Guernsey Evening Press* told its readers that the islands were being demilitarised and that the members of the Royal Guernsey Militia should hand in their uniforms and weapons and go home quietly. Confusion followed among the people and the authorities. People became angry and afraid as they realised they were being abandoned. Also on 19 June, it was announced that children of school age, younger children accompanied by their mothers, men of military age and 'all others' would have to register for evacuation that evening. My mother and I duly joined the queue to register at the town hall. Panic broke out however, as people tried to get their money from the banks. Despite the promises it was becoming clear that not all those wanting to leave would be able to do so. The authorities launched an anti-evacuation campaign. However, there were rumours that local doctors had warned that there would be food, water and health problems if Guernsey people stayed under German occupation. Opinions and moods changed from day to day.

My mother could not hold back the tears as we locked the house for the last time on 28 June, and carrying our suitcases walked towards the centre of St Peter Port. She had finally decided we ought to leave. We believed that Britain's cause would prevail and it would not be too long before our return. We joined a crowd of people at the quayside waiting in the glaring sun to be evacuated from St Peter Port. When the mail boat, the Isle of Sark, arrived we thought we were safe. But the crowd surged forward. A stampede threatened. As people were attempting to board we heard the engine noise of a plane. We looked up and we saw three planes approach. We did not know whether they were British or German. Our doubts vanished seconds later as bombs exploded in front of us. The policeman checking the boat tickets was literally blown to pieces. Others fell wounded as the area was sprayed with machine gun fire. We hid in a warehouse until the raid was over. By that time over 30 people lay dead and as many were wounded. That was my first brush with death and it wouldn't be my last. I couldn't believe the carnage left behind. I remember vividly the smell of burning flesh from the bullet holes - a smell that has lived with me throughout my life - and the cries of people who lay injured and dying.

The police advised us to return home, as no other ships would be arriving that day. So we did so. The harbour was bombed again the following day and then there was quiet. On that day and the days that followed attitudes changed. Many people lost faith in our local leaders and cursed the Churchill government in London. They thought we had been left in the lurch. Our faith in England was shaken. A German plane landed briefly at Guernsey's deserted airport on the afternoon of 30 June. Later that evening, the Germans returned in force and Inspector Sculpher of the Guernsey Police went to the airport and handed over a letter of surrender from the authorities. The occupation had begun.

I was one of only 1,100 school children left on Guernsey out of 7,000. You felt lonely, rejected, somehow inferior, because you were one of the minority still on the Island. You tended to blame your parents, in my case my mother, for this situation. Why were we the ones left behind? If only she had acted sooner. You saw the Island officials greeting, even kow-towing to the German officers and lost all respect for them and their system. Unknown to you they were, in most cases, merely trying to make life easier for the rest of us. Some islanders made anti-Semitic remarks about Dr W J Montague, who had left Guernsey for England. His detractors did not know that he had volunteered to stay but had been ordered to the mainland.

The Germans were under orders to behave well and they did so, destroying many of the propaganda stereotypes we had been fed. Gradually, the fear of them and reserve towards them broke down. 'They're all right, just doing their duty.' 'They're only human.' 'They pay for everything.' 'They're polite.' 'I feel sorry for them, I really do. They're only lads, most of 'em.' 'The officers are gentlemen. They try to speak English.' 'They don't interfere much.' 'It's not their fault Chamberlain declared war on them.' 'They no more want the war than we do.' These were typical comments. The Germans claimed the bombing of Guernsey and the other islands were a tragic mistake. They did not know the Channel Islands had been demilitarised. They had not been informed of this. The

British government had given it no publicity. Because they behaved well people started to believe them. The rationing of butter and some other foodstuffs ended and the banks, shops and cinemas re-opened as normal. The end of rationing was due to the favourable situation caused by the drop in population. It was not to last though.

There were few changes in school. Class sizes were greatly reduced which was an advantage, but not to us at the time. One or two favourite teachers had left either to supervise the evacuees or to join the armed services in England. Our French teacher 'Froggie the fool', a native French speaker of indeterminate background, who had a terrible wind problem, disappeared. That was one outlet of hilarity that we missed. On the other hand, 'Dick Snuff' was called out of retirement to resume Geography teaching. 'Loony Johnson' also returned, not forgetting his huge cane. We also got an Irish teacher, whom we quickly nick-named 'Old Mother O'Riley', with apologises to the comedian of that name, who helped out for a short time with German.

One day, early in 1941, we had a German visitor in the school who, although in civilian clothes, we thought was an official or officer or something of the kind. Shortly after that, the limited German teaching in our school was expanded. In 1942, it was made compulsory. I was one of the few who had been receiving instruction before the Germans arrived. I felt rather superior and smug after having put up with insults such as, 'Hello Martin Kraut' or 'Are you really a Jerry?' when my tormentors had to learn the language. They often came to me for help with their

German homework. I have to admit, that in schoolboy terms it became quite profitable. There was a war on after all!

Our failed attempt at evacuation helped in my liberation from my mother. In retrospect, I came to realise how difficult it must have been for her to know what to do for the best. We had no obvious place to go in England, no home and she had no immediate employment. Her brother had emigrated to Australia in the 1920s, while her cousins had left for South Africa about the same time. After the death of her father, her mother had joined the son in Sydney. Her sister had died of TB in the 1930s. She was not the type of person to land us on distant relatives whom she did not really know. The evacuation would have required leaving virtually everything behind with no security for the house or its contents. At the time, I had not thought about all this and decided that in future I must make decisions affecting me myself and not rely on my mother. Rather than confronting her, I simply went my own way without announcing it. In any case, my mother was becoming more difficult to live with. She became prey to headaches, tiredness and irritability. She had a struggle to keep employed after Mr Spencer's departure and had a series of part-time, temporary jobs.

I heard of the German attack on the Soviet Union on 22 June 1941 from the German radio. As I can never forget, they played Liszt's 'Les Preludes'. 'The war against Bolshevism had started…,' they proclaimed. I wondered what this meant. Most people had sympathised with Finland in its defence against Stalin. Now, Germany was fighting Stalin and Churchill was backing him. Would Chamberlain have done this I asked myself? After the attack on the Soviet Union more Germans started to come to Guernsey, some of them wounded.

After initially being slightly afraid of and shy of the enemy, we teenagers gained more self-confidence and simply ignored them in a slightly haughty way. My first direct encounter was in a paper shop where I saw a German in difficulties trying to buy cigarettes and postcards. He appeared the very opposite of the victorious high and mighty German that we had seen in the newsreels. In his early twenties, already balding and short of stature, he was recovering from a wound, and I could not help sympathising with him. I passed my first ever practical German test with flying colours. The downside of the encounter – though I did not recognise it at the time – was that he offered me one of his cigarettes, which I accepted. I bumped into him again a few days later sitting smoking on a bench and looking very lonely. We recognised each other and started chatting. This was the start of a friendship with Wolfgang from Cologne, who had been given an easy posting after a tough time in the Soviet Union. Although still young his face had that 'lived-in' look. Wolfgang said little about his experiences in Russia but my impression was that they had been awful. Much later, putting two and two together, I gathered it was not just the Red Army who had given him a bad time. He was haunted by the terrible things he had seen. His Catholic priest had warned him about the danger of going with 'girls of easy virtue', but not about the far greater threats to his immortal soul from being involved in Nazi crimes.

Wolfgang gave me a set of German stamps, which depicted the branches of the German armed forces. You could clearly make out the fine uniforms depicted on the stamps. They were very impressive and augmented the impression that Germany was an interesting place. I had been an avid stamp collector throughout my childhood and had a large collection thanks initially to my father who had always sent airmail issues from the many countries he flew to. They excited the imagination and led you to the inescapable conclusion that the world was a very interesting place. Yet I was stuck on this small island apparently with no chance of travelling anywhere.

After a few weeks Wolfgang went back to Germany. I received a post card from him and then nothing more. Our conversations greatly improved my German and, after he left, I was soon engaged in conversations with other Germans. I 'researched' the islands in the local library and became a kind of unofficial guide. Perhaps to some degree I sought the company of men because of the loss of my father and the sudden disappearance of Mr Spencer. Perhaps also I thought that through the Germans I could meet girls. They seemed to have no difficulties in finding local girls to go out with. These girls were despised by a section of the population and known, somewhat disparagingly, as 'Jerry bags'. But they were by no means always the worst looking or the least fashionable or the most poorly educated. I fancied one of these girls to whom I had been introduced by a German.

Dorothy worked in a local solicitor's office, which had some business contacts with the occupying power. I contrived to bump into to her as she was leaving work. She had wavy fair hair, blue eyes and was quite petite yet she had considerable personal authority. She was always well turned out; elegant is how I would describe her. I think some of the clothes she wore were her mother's, a fashionable lady who looked more like her elder sister than her mother. The mother had married an old man, who died leaving her well provided for. It was rumoured that perhaps Dorothy was not his daughter. We had a kind of friendship. We were both the 'only child'. We discussed life and the future but I could never quite steer our friendship into a romantic or sexual relationship although I desperately wanted to. Unfortunately, all we could do was go for walks, sometimes go for bike rides, sit chatting over a coffee in a snack bar or very occasionally go to the pictures. Dorothy, I remember most vividly, excited me on one or two occasions when she adjusted her silk stockings, probably a present from a German, and revealed her slender thighs, stocking tops and suspenders - this image remained with me for many years. I felt like a hero if I had managed to put my arm round her while we were resting in the countryside and she had not immediately released herself from my embrace. More often than not I would have to go home and fantasise about her to quench my sexual urges. Towards the end of our chaste friendship, she let me hold her hand for part of the journey home indicating that she wanted this by carrying her bag in her right hand when I was on her left side. I remember being able to smell the scent of her perfume on my hand for hours afterwards - it was intoxicating and something worth waiting for. Much to my disappointment though even this activity was a privilege and, like most other things on Guernsey at the time, was rationed. Had the war not intervened she, aged 17 and a product of Guernsey Ladies College (1872), would have been looking for a suitable husband. As it was she had little prospects. I was no use, being a year younger and 'inexperienced' and preparing for the Guernsey School Leaving Certificate.

Just about the only other woman I even talked to was a prostitute. She was one of a number brought over from France to entertain the German troops in an authorised brothel in St Peter Port. We saw the troops queuing to go in and wondered what exactly went on inside. These women, who were the only ones who really had the means, shopped in the town at all the most exclusive shops, especially the furrier where fur of all kinds - capes, coats, stoles wraps, accessories - were still available. I was thrilled to be able to help one through the vehicle of my school French. She was, one would say, quite attractive and gave me a kiss for my trouble. I became something of a local hero amongst my friends for even having got that far. I am not quite sure but I think I even felt somewhat 'grown-up' and walked taller. For the young people left behind in Guernsey life was becoming increasingly drab and boring. Food started to become less plentiful, clothes were in short supply, the cinemas had few films of interest and there were few organised activities for us. Worst of all, we felt imprisoned and forgotten on our remote island. We could not travel and news was scarce. The newspapers could only print the German version of events and wireless sets were confiscated, given back and then confiscated again. By early 1942, the Germans, and their new ally Japan, appeared to be winning hands down. The Japanese had captured the 'impregnable' fortress city of Singapore and Malaya and Hong Kong. They sunk the great British ships Prince of Wales and Repulse. With each day that passed the British Empire appeared to be crumbling. In addition, we were informed that they had inflicted heavy losses on the American fleet at Pearl Harbour (7 December. 1941). All seemed lost.

3.

Deportation to Biberach

I passed my Guernsey School Leaving Certificate in the summer of 1942. I was 16 and wondered what to do next. The prospects looked bleak. The jobs which would have been available before the war, working in a bank, local government, training to be a solicitor, local journalism, tourism, trying for a commission in the Army or continuing my education for university entry were all closed. With the two school friends I had I discussed the possibilities of escape but soon concluded that this was a hopeless cause. We were firmly trapped on the island. However, help was at hand from an unexpected source.

On 26 September 1942, the German authorities deported 825 men, women and children from Guernsey. My mother and I were among them. The official explanation was that this was a reprisal ordered by 'higher authority' for the internment of Germans in Iran. One of the first acts of the Anglo-Soviet Alliance was the invasion of neutral Iran in the summer of 1941. The British seized the Germans they found and interned them. As we were not native Channel Islanders, but British, we were thought to be suitable targets. Once again, we left our home with a suitcase each. This time there were no tears. We'd been told to take some warm clothing and footwear, food for the journey, and 'if possible' a blanket. We had to report at the *Gaumont* Cinema, where we had spent many happy hours and dreamed a few dreams. After having our particulars noted, we were escorted down to the harbour where we boarded a steamer for France. This time there was no rush. As the steamer made its way slowly out of St Peter Port, I asked myself, 'Will I ever see Guernsey again?'

The crossing was not without potential danger, as a number of boats had been sunk by the Royal Navy, but this journey proved uneventful. Many adults had anxiety written on their faces, a few were sea sick, but for me it was the beginning of a great adventure. After sailing through the night, we arrived in France at St. Malo. There we entrained into third class carriages and, after some checking and re-checking of documents, got under way. The journey seemed to last forever but for me was quite interesting. I had almost no experience of travelling by train. Apart from a day trip to France and a week in England when I was seven, I had not been away from the Islands since I was two. Despite the war, signs of which were everywhere, Germany appeared pleasant and prosperous. After a very long journey, with interruptions, we finally arrived at our destination, Biberach an der Riss in Bavaria, southern

Germany. The camp itself was officially *ILag V-B* or *Internierungslager* (internment camp) and had been built for the Hitler Youth movement in the 1930s, and prior to our arrival, had been used to hold British officer PoWs. The 23 barrack huts surrounded by a double barbed wire fence with watch towers and machine guns each held a maximum of 84 internees. In January 1943, the camp held 1,011 internees - 429 men, 437 women and 145 children. Initially, the camp was administered by the German Army, but in the spring of 1943 the administration was transferred to the Interior Ministry. This caused a worsening of food rations. On clear days there was a spectacular view of the Alps, which allowed us to dream a little.

At first, conditions in the camp were depressing for anyone who had been used to a lower middle class standard of comfort. The camp was infested with vermin, the sanitation was poor, it was cold and drafty and the food supply was not very generous. The barracks themselves were of an all-wooden construction with double bunks on either side of a walkway. Things improved somewhat after a visit by a representative of the Swiss Red Cross. Red Cross parcels started to arrive on a regular basis. I cannot say that the atmosphere created by the internees was good. They had too much time on their hands which led to petty arguments and gossiping. Paid work was offered, but virtually no one took it up. I wanted to but held back because mother did not think we would be popular if we accepted it. The camp was run by the inmates themselves and, to the credit of the leadership, they encouraged any number of activities including amateur dramatics, painting and lectures and they set up a school. In theory, sport was also possible, but at the beginning there was no equipment available. After a while we were allowed out several times a week in groups to go for walks in the beautiful Bavarian countryside and occasionally see something of the town. The area was made up of hilly countryside between the rivers of the Danube and the Iller. The town itself was surrounded by medieval walls and towers and was strikingly picturesque. There was a church dating from the 12th century that surprisingly possessed a hospital. The town's main industries were cloth, bell casting, toys and zinc wares, and its fruit markets were famous. The few local people we met were not unfriendly. Books were, at first, few and far between. Boredom forced you to read any and every publication you could lay your hands on, no matter how innocuous the subject. There were one or two paperback novels published in Leipzig in English. There were some German propaganda publications in English, which seemed to be aimed at prisoners-of-war. These even contained the British weekly football results. I read one or two detective stories loaned by fellow internees. One other volume I read was a book on psychiatry in which Sigmund Freud figured prominently. I found his theories fascinating and was given more food for thought some months later when I found out he was Jewish. Later the supply of books improved, both through the Red Cross and from German sources.

Having been born in Guernsey, Dorothy was not among the deportees and I was never to see her again. She was, nonetheless, regularly in my thoughts and I often wondered what became of her. There were other teenagers, among them girls, but I never got really close to any of them. Looking back I believe my mother was regarded as a danger by some of the married women whose husbands were with them. To me she was a very attractive lady and I feel this is how men saw her as well. Her position made it slightly more difficult for me to socialise.

4.

We have a visitor – John Amery

The camp was not without entertainment. There were concerts, sports and education classes. It had its own 11-piece orchestra. There were individual lectures and occasionally outside visitors. One such outside speaker was John Amery. Quite who invited him no one knew.

Of course, he had a distinguished name. Leo Amery was Cabinet Minister and Secretary of State for India and Burma, 1940-45, when we were sitting in the German camp. He had served in Conservative governments as Colonial Secretary, 1924-29, and before that had been in charge of Britain's great fleet. To the elder internees, therefore, his was a well-known name. It was presumed that the son, John, had some kind of mandate from the father. His visit one afternoon drew a sizeable audience. Starved of news other than what the Germans cared to tell them, the internees hoped to hear firsthand about the situation at home and about the government's thinking on how to bring about peace.

They certainly heard about a possible road to peace, but it was not Churchill's, nor was it that of the British government. It was the view of the son, John Amery. He wanted Britain to make peace with Germany and join it in a crusade against the Soviet Union and Communism. He was quite eloquent, '...the priceless heritage of our fathers, of our seamen, of our Empire builders, is being thrown away in a war that serves no British interests'. The alliance with Stalin was an alliance with a regime that was out to destroy us. He rejected the idea that by working with Germany one would be committing treason. How could it be treason to attempt to stop your country being destroyed? He spent much of his time visiting British prisoners of war and internees hoping to convert them to his cause. The handsome, 30-year-old English gentleman, who looked as if he had been to the same school, same tailor and same hairdresser as David Niven rather than Adolf Hitler, impressed me. I could imagine that the Daily Mail, the Duke of Windsor and Mr Spencer would have endorsed his general line of thought. There was a moment of hesitation at the end of Amery's talk followed by ragged, half-hearted, polite applause. Some of the audience were sympathetic, most were confused or neutral or did not know what to think. There was this nagging feeling in some minds that he must be there with the private, even secret, blessing of the British government or at least parts of it. Sadly for Amery, they were wrong and he was hanged as a traitor after the war. After the lecture, I had a conversation with Amery, which was to change my life.

He was quite a glamorous figure to me and with him he had his glittering and elegant French lover, Jeannine Barde, who nodded in approval when he made a point. Given my political background, such as it was, his basic political line made sense. He told me he expected that a British Legion of St George would be formed to fight as an SS unit against the Bolsheviks, and that I would have a great future in it. There was no possibility of us fighting against Britain. It had been suggested that Brigadier-General Leonard Parrington of the British Army would lead the legion. The stylish man in the tweed suit, herringbone shirt with woven tie, and his beautiful companion had won me over. I needed to break the news to my long-suffering mother.

My mother was anxious. She said she could not judge the politics, but felt I was too young, that it did not seem quite right 'somehow'. But, I guess I was so bored and yearned for change that I argued and pleaded strongly. Did I not have my father's example? Would I not be following in his footsteps? These were my rhetorical questions. The war would soon end and we would be together again. She realised it was hopeless and gave me her blessing. Amery did the rest. We agreed that for my mother's sake there would be no publicity at this stage. It would just be said that I had gone to work elsewhere in Germany.

I was sent to the local military recruitment commission where I was required to join a group of young Germans who had got their call-up papers. We were told to undress and filed one by one with our papers as our only covering before a five-member medical board. Elementary health questions were asked about sexually transmitted diseases and other impediments and the sexual organs, lungs, teeth, eyes, ears and feet were all examined. One of the doctors, wearing SS uniform, took special interest in me. I later wondered if he'd perhaps been homosexual. 'Typical Nordic islander,' he said in a superior sort of way, 'fair hair, blue eyes, thin longish face. Fantastic.' We were asked for our military preferences and which branch of the services did we want to serve in. There was some surprise when I said 'Waffen SS'. But a smug smile lit up the SS doctor's face. Little did I know that by that time, early in 1943, the parents of most young Germans were not overly anxious for their sons to join the SS. This was partly because of the high casualty rate. My preference was duly noted and I was told I would be informed in due course whether I had been successful.

Days later, I was contacted not by post but in person. A military-style man in his forties in civilian clothes, wearing a smart tweed sports jacket, trousers, a v-neck pullover and a sombre tie, was waiting for me in the Biberach camp office. He announced himself as SS liaison officer Schmidt and said it was his pleasant duty, in the name of the *Reichsführer* SS Heinrich Himmler, to inform me that I had been successful in my application to join the Waffen

SS. He paused, looked straight at me with his pale-blue eyes, to gauge my reaction. Surprised, excited and slightly embarrassed, I said nothing. Schmidt then made a short speech in which he said I was going to serve not only Germany but Europe and even England. When the war was over, he assured me, we would all be together in the *Europäische Wirtschaftsgemeinschaft* (the European Economic Community). I was issued with a travel permit entitling me to second class travel by train to Hamburg *Hauptbahnhof* (main railway station). He also gave me an envelope containing a quantity of *Reichsmark* to pay for my subsistence. Finally, I was given a temporary identity card. After I had signed various documents he gave me a half-arm 'Heil Hitler!' greeting. I hesitated for a second and then gave a brisk, 'Heil Hitler!' but he was already gone.

5.

Volunteer: Life in the 'European Army'

The journey on the crowded train in the blackout was long, but I greatly enjoyed it. It was an adventure in itself. After the tedious months in the camp it was a great relief to be able to see so much. I felt like a king. When two Gestapo officials checked our papers they seemed impressed by my ID and thus so did the other passengers. My carriage appeared to have a constant plume of cigarette smoke swirling round it: this was mainly due to one middle-aged, perhaps business man, chain smoking his way through the journey whilst constantly looking out of the window and at the compartment's door in a harassed manner. He was a fair-haired, reasonably presented, gentleman of about 35, with a moustache. As we travelled he seemed to be constantly in possession of a cigarette, with his attaché case clutched closely to his chest. I wondered who he was, what he was doing and where he was going. One or two other passengers contributed to this continuous swirl over time. But there was little conversation. The second class compartments were upholstered, the third were not. People looked at me as it was unusual for a lone teenager, even more so one in civilian clothes, to be travelling second class. The money was more than enough for my needs and, at the end of the journey, I still had a few marks over.

The Hamburg Hauptbahnhof seemed immense; a hive of activity with people rushing in all directions. There were young men in the navy blue of the *Kriegsmarine*, there other young men in the light blue of the Luftwaffe, and there were many more, on average older men, in army grey. There were a few in black SS uniforms. Even the *Reichbahn* ticket collectors were smartly turned out in blue with peaked caps. A group of Hitler Youth passed me as I stood bewildered on the platform. There were also many well-dressed men and women in civilian clothes on their way to or from work. In addition to commercial adverts for toothpaste, cigarettes and clothes, the station was festooned with slogans such as *Es lebe Deutschland!* and surprisingly, *Wir werden nie Kapitulieren!* (We will never surrender).

From the main station I made my way by tram to the SS barracks in Hamburg-Langenhorn. The journey took about 40 minutes. Upon arriving, I still remember how jittery I felt as I stepped smartly under the arch, showed my papers to the sentry and was directed to the main administration office. No one appeared to be expecting me and after what seemed to be a long wait and several telephone calls an SS officer, a *Hauptsturmführer* or captain, came to greet me. Slightly mockingly, he reproved the duty NCO for not having found me some refreshment. He took me to the officers' Casino and provided me with beer and potato salad - it wasn't bad and was most welcome by this time. It took him some time to take it in that I really was English and not just a German who had lived in Britain, or someone of mixed parentage. I spent the night in a small room with a camp bed, a wooden locker and not much else. I slept in fits and starts. I must have been anxious. What new experiences was tomorrow going to bring?

Next morning, saying very little, a corporal took me for breakfast with my 'comrades', most of whom were non-Germans, after which I was taken to another office. There, another officer asked me questions about myself, background, how I had acquired my excellent German, why I had decided to volunteer and so on. He made several telephone calls and I started to think I had become an administrative problem. I would have loved to dare to say, 'I don't want to be a problem, let me go back to the camp.'

There was some discussion as to the unit with which I should serve. 'The Finns?', 'Out of the question!', 'the Flemings?', 'Too rough!', 'the Norwegians?', 'No vacancies.', 'the Danes?', 'Good idea!'. The Danes it was. That, however, was not the end of the story. The Danes had been moved. They were no longer in Hamburg but in Breslau. The officer apologised saying there was nothing to be done, I must go to Breslau. A travel warrant and more marks were duly issued and, without much ceremony, I was taken by *Kubelwagen*, a wartime variant of the Volkswagen, back to the main station. This time, perhaps by an oversight, my ticket was third class.

I was soon on my way to Breslau in the east via Berlin and Görlitz. The giant steam engine meandered slowly through the countryside. Several times it was forced into sidings or onto branch lines to make way for troop or munitions trains. Only in Berlin, where I changed, could I buy anything to eat or drink. My brief stop in Berlin was extended because of a British air raid during which I spent several cramped hours in a shelter. It was my first experience of a proper air raid and not one I was in a hurry to repeat. Eventually, I got underway again on a train made up of 'double-decker' coaches and I arrived in Breslau half-asleep and thoroughly exhausted several hours later.

As I was leaving the main station in Breslau I passed a group of Soviet prisoners under guard. They looked in very bad shape, dirty, unshaven, half-starved, their clothes little better than rags and the stench was something, particularly when standing downwind. I reasoned that even if they had been in poor condition when taken captive it would not have cost much to replace their clothing and feed them and thus win them over for the anti-Bolshevik cause.

I did not know at the time that I had had a narrow escape. Within days of my departure from Hamburg in July 1943 it suffered a devastating raid by the RAF and the US Army Air Force. Over 40,000 civilians were killed in a single night. I could have been one of them!

The SS in Breslau were expecting me and without much greeting or formality I was shown my billet with the other new recruits. Our quarters, though modern, were rather Spartan. In the dining hall Himmler looked down at us rather mournfully from a wall. Hitler was depicted in his many heroic roles. We saw him patting a small boy on the head, surrounded by young women, as the friend of all dogs, as a connoisseur of art and as the chief strategist of the Reich putting his generals straight. We were kited out with standard SS uniforms, which disappointed some volunteers, who had expected to have various arm-shields and or collar badges, but these seemed to be in short supply. I must confess I was a little disappointed myself as I remember how colourful and striking the uniforms had appeared on the stamps my father had once sent to me. Nevertheless, they were of excellent quality. Later we were paraded and required to swear our oath of allegiance to Adolf Hitler in his fight against Bolshevism. We had already been assured we would not have to fight against our own countries. The oath was conducted in a solemn manner with precision and passion. Afterwards I certainly felt part of something special.

My platoon was made up mainly but not exclusively of Danes. Language was not a problem for me as several spoke English and most of them spoke some German.

Several had served in the Danish armed forces and we turned to them for guidance on everything from cleaning our weapons to military jargon and conduct. We were part of the Panzer-Grenadier-Regiment (motorised infantry) 'Danmark' which in turn was part of the SS division Nordland. It is a cliché that all NCOs bellow and humiliate recruits and those in the Waffen SS were no exception. How many times did we hear that we were like a bunch of old Jews, nothing better than maggots, lumps of shit and urged to straighten up and stop drooping like sacks of rubbish! It has to be said that our NCO did not discriminate against any particular nationality; he gave the impression of hating all his charges equally. If anything, he felt more uneasy with the former members of the Danish Army. He had seen action, they had not, but their elementary skills meant that he had to be on his toes the whole time and he had to be more sparing when recalling his front-line experiences. Being the only one of my 'race', I was something of a celebrity and I have no doubt that I had it easier for that reason. Others faced bullying from instructors and from each other, which I did not. It was also an advantage to be the youngest.

Later, when I got to know more of my comrades, their motivations, backgrounds and personal histories, I realised we were a very mixed bunch. Some, like me, came from basically anti-Communist backgrounds, liked the idea of a united Europe to prevent further warfare and sought to better themselves by joining up. Others were simply running away from personal problems either with their families or from the law. A spirit of adventure was a common feature, as was a lack of knowledge about what war was really like. We had all been influenced by the swift success of the Germans in the first years of the war and by the apparent modernity of German ways.

As part of our ideological training we were shown propaganda newsreels designed to expose the British, the Americans and the Jews. These were *Gentlemen*, *Rund um die Freiheitsstatue* (Round the Statue of Liberty) and *Der ewige Jude*. I felt uneasy watching *Gentlemen* which attacked, among others, Churchill and Eden. The sinking of the French fleet at Oran in 1940 by the British was something I knew nothing of. The commentator also alleged the British had badly damaged Louvain University library during their retreat. *Der ewige Jude* (The Eternal Jew) was for me the least effective. I knew little of 'the Jewish question', only that back home some people had not particularly liked Jews, but it was not a major issue. I found the film a fairly incoherent hotchpotch of anti-Semitic images, including one depicting the Jews as rats. Even then, I could not help thinking, 'surely there must be some good Jews . . . Jesus? Freud?' For some reason the exposure of the Soviet Union took the form of a photographic display. Perhaps as the Soviets, like the Nazis, carefully censored every film image, no suitable Soviet footage was available. The exhibition was of the Katyn Wood Massacre, which had recently been unearthed and had first been announced on Radio Berlin in April 1943. On Stalin's orders thousands of Polish officers (about 4,500) had been shot there in 1940. Only in the 1980s did Moscow admit to the crime. The most devastating of the films was an attack on the USA. It appeared to be entirely made up of American footage. It showed the use of force against strikers, World War I veterans, who demanded the payment of bonuses being dispersed by cavalry, tanks and gas, farmers being forced off their land for failing to repay bank loans, farmers pouring milk into the gutter, mass unemployment and decadent American art and practices such as women wrestling in mud! One other clever piece of propaganda I recall was the feature film, *Ohm Krüger*, starring the internationally famous actor Emil Jannings. It was about the Boer War and was made as an expose of aggressive British Imperialism. It depicted British concentration camps where thousands of Boer women and children had died. I had never heard of this before but was very shocked by it. We were also shown an adventure film, which had the Irish struggle for independence against the British as its background. Although my mother was of southern Irish Protestant background she had not been unsympathetic to the cause of Irish independence. I vaguely knew there had been an armed struggle. I was, therefore, receptive to the film's message. The main emphasis, however, of our ideological training was on the battle to save Europe from Asiatic Bolshevism and our common future in a united Europe, a Europe free of poverty and unemployment, where the common good prevailed over personal selfishness.

After completing our basic training we were allowed out to see the bustling ancient city of Breslau, the pre-war population of 625,000 having been swollen by refugees, foreign workers and the armed forces. Breslau, Heidi, an attractive pre-war guide now an air force auxiliary, informed us, was the most important city not only in Silesia, but also in the whole of eastern Germany. Our first outing was an organised coach trip followed by a short boat journey down the busy river Oder. The press and radio came along and later one or two photographs appeared in the local newspaper and probably in the forces' magazine Signal. Our other 'treat' was a soldiers' night out, which included heavy drinking and a visit to a well-known brothel. For me it was my first time, though I was too embarrassed to admit the fact. It was a challenge, which I failed. Our 'madam' or hostess was over-weight, over-dressed and over the hill. I asked myself about this heavily made-up creature with the rubbery lips, 'Is it a man in all those frilly numbers or just a rather masculine woman?' Constantly stopping to catch her breath, she assured us that all was on offer and any special services could be catered for. As she spoke and drained her glass of white wine, several of the 'girls' hung around circling us and eying us up like prey. They were all shapes, sizes and colours; blondes, brunettes and red heads. From their clothes and hair-styles they were clearly hoping they would remind us of Marlene Dietrich, Betty Grabble, Vivian Leigh, Zarah Leander or Viviane Romance, the first and the last of whom had played in films as highly seductive whores. Certainly, in my case they failed. One or two of the other lads were luckier. 'My' girl did not entice or excite me, she was rather coarse and certainly no beauty. Although she appeared to be a good deal older than me she did not show too many signs of experience. She was far removed from the glamorous divas on the silver screen or from one or two of the women I'd seen going into the Hotel Kronprinz in Breslau. Heidi, in her ill-fitting uniform, had looked more fetching. Despite the advice from my girl to relax - a difficult operation in itself with all the grunts and groans coming through the paper-thin walls - and to think about my girlfriend and then her offer of 'a little bit of help', I couldn't make it. Finally, in exasperation she offered me 'a blow job'. This I rejected without really knowing what I had turned down. Flustered and slightly embarrassed I pulled up my pants and trousers and left. I would be going into battle still a virgin.

6.

Baptism of Fire

Our journey to the front was by train, truck and then on foot. It was the autumn of 1943. The Sixth Army had already perished at Stalingrad. Worse still, in material terms, was the defeat at Kursk in the summer months of July and August. The Battle of Kursk remains both the largest series of armoured clashes and the most costly single day of aerial warfare to date. It was the last Blitzkrieg offensive we (the Germans) were able to execute in the East. From then on this decisive Soviet victory gave the Red Army the strategic initiative, which it was able to maintain for the remainder of the war. We were being thrown in, in a vain attempt to stem the relentless and increasingly aggressive Soviet attacks.

I do not know how my comrades felt on the way to the front. I only know that I had a feeling of emptiness in my stomach. I always suffered in this way in moments of extreme tension and dread. I had experienced it before school exams. This was another kind of exam; at least, that's the way I attempted to rationalise the situation to overcome my fear. Whether this sensation was caused by fear alone or by excitement I have never been able to decide.

We marched through the night, a tiring exercise in itself, and early in the morning reached a farmhouse where we bivouacked in the adjacent orchard. As we ate our rations we could hear the noise of gunfire. There was the dull thud of artillery, which our NCO identified as our own 150mm guns. Suddenly, as if from nowhere, came the deafening roar of low flying planes unloading their deadly payload of rockets and bombs. They were undoubtedly the heavily armed Sturmovik ground support bombers of the Red Army air force, which we came to fear and respect. Luckily, we were not the target. The victims were the lines of troops wending their way in single file along the edge of the road and the horse-drawn supply wagons and artillery in the middle of it. I was certain that we could hear the screams of those being blown to pieces in the distance being carried on the light wind, but our NCO dispelled any such thoughts. This was my third air raid and it was far worse than the first two. Later as we marched off, we passed the shattered vehicles and men and animals lying dead or dying. Death had left its victims in many different postures and shapes. At the one extreme there were the 'movie' dead, hit by a single bullet or fragment, which revealed little visible sign of their fate. At the other extreme there were those without faces, those with their intestines hanging out, those with limbs blown off and those whose physical remains had simply been blown apart. I think I had been right but at the same time I think our NCO had just wanted to keep our minds focused. For us young, inexperienced soldiers it was total immersion into the hell of war.

As Messerschmitt BF 109G fighters drove off the attacking Sturmoviks, we continued along the hot dusty road. We passed through all that remained of a village with its gutted church and burned out cottages, some of which were still smouldering. There were more corpses. I felt panic and my stomach was getting knotted with fear. Could anyone survive here? The road wound upwards between hills on both sides. Presently, we left the road to the right and climbed up a steep path. Before we reached the summit however we suffered our first fatality. The tallest of our unit, an Austrian from Linz, like most of us not wearing his helmet, was killed instantly by a volley of rifle fire. The 7.92mm light machine gun, which had been slung over his shoulder, was down the hill immediately. My heart rate increased, as did the adrenalin now pumping round my body. We quickly took cover and struggled to put on our helmets. We crawled the last few metres to the top on our bellies with dust and dirt in our faces and joined our comrades in a trench. Although they had a heavy machine gun mounted, we all kept our heads down in the face of concentrated enemy rifle and machine gun fire. The fire went on relentlessly all day. Through his binoculars our team leader saw ever increasing numbers of enemy infantry and some cavalry crossing the valley below and moving towards us. They were backed by T-34 tanks. From our side two or three Tigers attempted to slow the Soviet advance. Although not as well built as the Tigers, the T-34s' sheer weight in numbers would soon overwhelm them. It was only a matter of time. As one enemy unit was dug in on a hill opposite us, there was little we could do other than occasionally fire off blindly and then duck again. The heat and the tension wore us down. It was the longest day of my life. We were grateful to be alive as darkness fell.

I'm sure we all prayed that the order to withdraw would come that night. Silently, each man with his own thoughts, we held on shivering from cold and fear. The firing was now just intermittent but we jumped at every sound. With difficulty we pulled our blankets around us. Occasionally, a flare would illuminate the night sky and there would be some more sustained bursts of fire before silence prevailed once more. The night seemed as long and as terrifying as the day. As dawn broke, we lay there tired, hungry, thirsty and wanting to relieve ourselves. Feeling dazed I stood up for a second, putting my right hand up to adjust my helmet. In an instant my hand felt as if it were on fire. My watch was shattered and there was a hole in my sleeve. A piece of bullet protruded from my hand along with what looked like a piece of bone. I could not stop shaking and cursing with pain. 'Oh fuck, fuck . . . fuck, Jesus Christ, someone help me, help me I'm hit!' Luckily for me, there was a medical orderly in the trench who quickly covered the wound with a field dressing and gave me a large swig of brandy. At last the order to withdraw came. Why had they waited until daybreak? Once again, we were under heavy fire. One by one we crawled out of the trench and made our way down the very same path we'd struggled to get to not more than 24 hours previously. As we reached the road our numbers were reduced still further by a hail of bullets that spattered around us. I passed out as another hit me. Later I discovered the bullet had passed through my calf narrowly missing the shin bone. When I regained consciousness, I was on my feet and being almost dragged, at pace, by a comrade down the road. I could hardly walk. I had almost forgotten about my injuries because by now fear had taken over and it was my adrenaline that was keeping me going. In the rubble of the nearby village I was loaded on to a Mercedes truck with a few other poorly looking Wehrmacht, SS and allied personnel. As the shells rained in on us it seemed like an eternity before we were finally underway heading in a westerly direction. It was a bumpy, at times, murderous drive. I cursed the driver but I was grateful to be on that truck and moving away from that living hell. We passed through dozens of one-street villages, most of which were burned out or shortly to be so. We passed some of their bewildered inhabitants whose fate was uncertain. Just because they were still alive they were under suspicion from both sides. We drove past thousands of our own men, Germans, Italians, Romanians, Slovaks, French, Danes and others from decimated units heading in the same direction. As I looked out from the truck, the lines of retreating troops seemed to stretch for miles. Now and again we were stopped by the *Feldgerdarmerie* looking for deserters, infiltrators or spies, but they quickly waived us on after a cursory glance at our papers. One or two others on foot were not so lucky, but sadly by then, I was beyond caring about others. All the strength I had left was consumed by my grim determination to hang on to life. I was never to get so far East in a German uniform again. I never wanted to. I was never to see most of my comrades again. It was a chilling experience.

7.

Königsberg 'Prisoner' of the girls of the 'Sanidad Militar'

By the time I fully came to I was off the lorry and on a train. It was long, dimly lit and full of wounded, many in much worse shape than me. The smell of decaying flesh, death and, not least, general uncleanliness had, at first, been intolerable but I grew used to it. I woke up several times due to the jolting of the train, the groaning, snoring, muttering, mumbling, whimpering and occasional cries for help from the other travellers, some on their last journey. Four or five times a nurse came and fed me broth. It was not pleasant but it did the job. We travelled for probably about 36 hours before reaching our final destination, the Baltic port of Königsberg. It was the capital of eastern Prussia from the Late Middle Ages until 1945 when it was repopulated and then in 1946 renamed Kaliningrad by the Soviets.

A convoy of ambulances and trucks awaited us at the side of the modern station, the *Nordbahnhof* and soon we were underway again. After a short drive of about 15 minutes we were unloaded at a military hospital. The formalities were few and as it was already dark we were put to bed and left for the night. I soon went into a deep sleep. Perhaps I felt safe at last and could relax and enjoy the luxury of sleep, clean sheets and a bed. Perhaps we had been given a sleeping draught; I do not know.

With a bright but cool sun shining in my face I woke in the antiseptic atmosphere of the church-like ward. The nurse wore a uniform rather different from those on the train. Her head-dress consisted of a khaki wimple and white coif upon which was pinned a silver-grey metal badge bearing the words 'Sanidad Militar'. The same words were inscribed on her belt buckle. Her uniform, blouse and pleated skirt, were also khaki. A friendly smile crossed her intelligent face and she asked in German if I was feeling better. I said I was and asked where I was. She told me this was the main hospital in Königsberg and that she was Lieutenant Nurse Sagrado of the Spanish Army Medical Corps. Most of the patients in this particular wing were Spanish volunteers, but there was also an assortment of other foreign troops. Presently, a German doctor accompanied by a Spaniard, both lean figures in their 30s with their white medical robes covering their uniforms, reached my bed.

The German asked, 'You really English?'

'*Ja, Ich bin Engländer*,' was my prompt reply.

'*Ah, wunderbar, Sie sprechen Deutsch.*' He went on, 'My English, not good, school only, you understand?' Relieved he switched to German. He told me I'd recover totally, but that my left leg, as well as my right hand, were 'in a bit of a mess' and that I could look forward to getting to know Königsberg well before returning to duty. 'Enjoy it, I think you've deserved it,' he said and with a knowing double wink of both his eyes continued, 'there are many delights here.'

Over the next few weeks I savoured the delights to the extent that I was tended by several nurses from the Sanidad Militar and by two German nurses. To me, a 17 year-old with hardly any experience of women, let alone sex, they all looked extremely desirable. Their close proximity, gentle touch, scent and occasional embarrassment heightened my sense of their desirability. If anything, their uniforms seemed to enhance their femininity. This was also true of Lieutenant Nurse Sagrado with her more authoritative and usually business-like manner. Whereas she was already at the end of her twenties the Germans were still in their teens. I too was sometimes embarrassed. It was not easy to ask for a bedpan and then relieve yourself in front of these lovely creatures. And when they changed your pants it was not easy to feign indifference. On one occasion Lieutenant Sagrado asked me how I was feeling when one of her subordinates was changing me. 'Oh, I'm delighted to see you like us,' she said teasingly.

After countless inspections by the German and Spanish doctors sometimes separately, sometimes together, followed by physiotherapy and exercise, I was allowed out of the hospital. A tram took me into town and I felt everyone was looking at me during the journey. The other passengers were mostly older civilians or children. The conductress, a friendly young woman, who said she was Swiss, gave me a few tips on where to go. With the aid of a stick and a pre-war guide book, loaned by Hauptmann Dr Christian Adam, I gradually saw the sights including the university and the tomb of philosopher Emil Kant, the castle of the Knights of the Teutonic Order, the Amber Museum, 'the only museum of its kind in the world', and the famous docks with the largest corn silos on the Continent. This city, like the other German towns I had seen, confirmed my view that Germany was cleaner, more modern, better organised and enjoyed a higher standard of living than Britain. Up to that time Königsberg had avoided the mass bombing which cities in western Germany had been forced to face.

I felt very guilty that I had not been in touch with my mother, so I wrote her a postcard. This was not easy because I had never actually written to anyone before. On the back of a postcard depicting the castle I managed:

Dear Mummy,
I am staying in Königsberg for a few weeks. It is a beautiful city.
I am very well. The people here are very kind. Would you believe
it, I've met some Spaniards! They are also very kind. I hope
you're well.
Lots of love. Martin.

One day the good Doctor bumped into me in the corridor outside the ward. 'I've been looking for you. Two things: I've heard you are due for a medal; second, I'm inviting you to a soirée tomorrow evening. It's about time you got around a bit. I'll arrange for you to be absent from the hospital.' He wrote down the address and told me to be ready at 19.30 next evening when I would be picked up. All went according to plan and just before 20.00 I found myself being greeted at the door of a large detached house in the well-known Jugendstil in Ratshof, on the outskirts of the city.

Although this was a mixed gathering of all ages and both sexes, older people tended to predominate. Most of them seemed to know each other well and did not hesitate to attack the buffet when it arrived. Given that this was the fourth year of the war, it was lavish with a variety of salami, ham, cheese, salad and breads. The hostess was none other than the Doctor's young aunt, the widow Hilde Reinhardt. Though very attractive she seemed much older than me at the time. Looking back, she could not have been more than 30 to 35. She was an elegant lady of substance with blond hair and unusual green eyes. A forceful personality, she was obviously used to be deferred to by those around her. I was fascinated by her and I suppose she expected that. Speaking in English she said, 'So very nice to have you with us. Christian has told me so much about you and your exploits.' I was flattered but wondered what was meant by 'my exploits'. Although any number of the other guests shook my hand, regretted the war, recalled fond memories of visits to England or of English friends, Christian and his aunt kept returning to see that I was being looked after. A local member of the Reichstag, Erich Fuchs, was getting worked up over Churchill, 'He was a Liberal now he's a Conservative. He supported Fascism in the 1920s, now he supports Bolshevism. I ask you, can you understand that Herr Thomas?' Before I was forced to reply, the hostess pulled me out of the circle to have another glass of vintage *Sekt*. Not used to *Sekt*, I soon felt slightly inebriated. As the guests began to leave, Frau Reinhardt exclaimed in a theatrical way to her nephew, 'The boy stays here! It would be barbaric to send the little hero (*der kleine Held*) back to that hospital tonight. He can't remain a prisoner of those Sanidad Militar girls. How can they help him!' Christian was certainly not saying anything different having already arranged for me to be absent.

After all the guests had gone we sat together on a sofa sipping 'one last drink' and talking about everything and nothing. After stroking my upper thigh and skilfully getting her hand in the right place in my trousers the lady said, 'You're a lovely young man and so innocent. Come, we're going to bed. We'll cuddle a bit and see what happens.' Full of obvious excitement, I felt certain, at last, I was going to become a man that night. I was not to be disappointed.

Having got leave arranged for me by Dr Adam, I spent most of the next two weeks at Frau Hilde's villa. She fed me, bedded me on a regular basis and gave me an education, which was to stand me in good stead for the rest of my life. Her laughter when I described my brothel experiences was in no sense ridicule and she initiated me into the art of the 'blow job'. I was amazed to discover that the tongue was as potent a sexual weapon as the penis, that the 'missionary position' was just one of several options and that bondage and chastisement could be very stimulating when the one in charge was an experienced practitioner. Frau Hilde certainly knew her way around the sexual maze. She told me how she had been seduced by an older man, a friend of the family and a de Sade devotee, when she was a schoolgirl. He had left her with a taste for both giving and receiving the lash as a 'purifying experience'. She quoted sentences from the mad Marquis's works, which, with only school certificate French, I did not readily grasp the meaning of. She was by temperament curious and ready to experience all that life could offer. She was a natural teacher who, in other circumstances, would have ended up either on the stage or teaching at a great university. I went about with a permanent smile on my face – or was it just a silly grin? The Ukrainian maid did not betray any sense of shock at our antics. But my education was not only sexual. This was a woman of culture who was anxious to be known as such and was delighted that she had found someone ready to receive her ideas on the arts, literature, philosophy, recent history, the organisation of the state and, above all, the way modern people ought to live. She was a disciple of Nietzsche rather than of Kant and she made it clear to me that she was no crude follower of National Socialism. Not being initiated into the finer points of German politics, I could only vaguely follow her argument that it was time the best elements of the Nazi party and the armed forces took control of the fate of Germany. 'Bad things are being done and stupid mistakes are being made. Hitler doesn't know what's going on. I'm sure of that. Don't be shocked Martin when I say such things and don't ever repeat them.' At that stage I was not clear what she meant and was too embarrassed to ask or contradict her. I had seen stupid mistakes made by our officers and I had wondered about some of the dead civilians I had seen. Who had killed them and why? However, I also had a feeling of vague unease about this critical messenger's life of luxury and my enjoyment of it. It was easy to be an arm chair critic of a leadership who were straining every sinew to defend the country against the most powerful countries in the world.

Over the days I got to know the Villa Reinhardt a little. Its living room was as large as the entire ground floor of my childhood home. The parquet floor was covered in oriental rugs. There were several sofas and a grand piano. Original works of art lined the walls. Years later, I realised the nude I had seen was almost certainly one by Adolf Ziegler. On the night of the party Hilde had caught my embarrassment on seeing the painting; her other guests were used to it. She later confided in me that that was the moment she decided she definitely wanted me to stay. Unlike the main room the kitchen was of a highly modern design; what I was later to identify as Bauhaus. The hostess proved to be a good cook. The bathroom we used was also in the Bauhaus style. There, I discovered that one of the few luxuries Frau Hilde kept for herself was toilet paper. In the cloakroom guests had to put up with neatly cut pieces of the Nazi paper *Völkischer Beobachter*. The large bedroom was how I visualised a Parisian bedroom, slightly decadent and beautifully finished. Another considerable room was filled with books not just in German, but also in English and French covering the arts, politics, history and travel. Any number of novelists were represented including writers, unknown to me at the time, no longer favoured by the regime, such as Thomas Mann and Erich Kästner. As I was later to read his works, I remember seeing several of Upton Sinclair's books, which were highly critical of American society. Another book I was surprised to see was by Sigmund Freud. I must admit, I was a bit intimidated by so much knowledge in such a small space and by the thought that perhaps Frau Hilde had read most of those books.

Frau Hilde's husband had been killed in Poland in 1939. Having run a family business important for the war effort, he need not have gone, but as an officer of the reserve he felt compelled to do so. She explained that they had greatly admired each other but had pursued an 'open marriage'. She took me to my first symphony concert to see Fürtwängler conduct Beethoven's Third in the *Stadthalle* and also to the zoo and to the famous wine restaurant in the basement of the Castle known ominously as *Das Blutgericht* (The Blood Court). I met Hilde's sister who looked at me and then gave her a knowing smile. However, although the Doctor assured me that I needed rest and relaxation, I started to feel like a shirker. I needed to get back to my comrades and see it through.

At last I was 'allowed' to leave. Hilde went with me to the collection point in Königsberg. She tied her pale blue, French, silk scarf around my neck. Trying to be jokey, she said, 'I'd give you something else of mine but it would not look too good if you had kitbag inspection.' She also gave me a two-mark piece in mint condition; on the back was President Hindenburg, on the front was the German eagle with the Nazi Swastika. The date on the coin was 1939. Around the edge was engraved, 'The common good goes before private good.' To my annoyance at the time, I lost the scarf on the great retreat in 1944. The coin became a kind of talisman and I still have it. Then moved by the terrible reality of parting and with a tear in her eye Hilde whispered, 'Come back soon.' I have to admit I'd become quite close to Hilde in such a short time and could not say much as my stomach had butterflies, and I had a lump in my throat with the realisation of my imminent departure. Furthermore, I had no idea if I'd see her again.

From the collection centre we were taken to parade with other recently wounded at the Tannenberg National Monument, an immense construction designed to perpetuate the memory of the victory of the German armies led by Field-Marshal Hindenburg and General Ludendorff over the Russians in August in 1914. We were billeted in one of the eight massive towers, which had been a youth hostel before the war. The following day we paraded to receive our 'Eastern Front Wounded' medal from a general whose name I have long since forgotten. He stopped in front of me and said in English, 'We value your courage. Sadly, there are not enough of you.' After the presentation there was more refreshment and then we climbed aboard the waiting truck to be taken direct to the *Nordbahnhof* and back to the uncertainties of war.

8.

The evil that men do

Since the summer of 1943 there had been a complete role reversal on the eastern front; the Soviets had become the attackers and we the defenders. We had been pushed back from Russia and the Ukraine into Poland. Once again, I was slightly wounded, again in the hand, but this time I was soon back at the front. By that time we had become a mixed bunch drawn together from various other units. Our unit even included two or three Spaniards. More significantly, we had a sprinkling of former regular police officers, who had been simply drafted into the SS without any choice. As their original (police) units had been badly mauled they had been ordered to join us. As a regular fighting unit we were at first a little suspicious of them. My Nordland comrades did not mind the tough fighting - some even enjoyed it - but most were not happy about 'anti-Partisan police actions.' All too often this resulted in the killing of women and children rather than combatants. We had heard of the terrible slaughter in Warsaw of men, women and children following the defeat of the Polish rising in 1944. The rape, murder, torture and fire had gone on even after SS General, Erich von dem Bach Zelewski, himself notorious, had ordered an end to the carnage. His Cossacks and criminals were out of control. I thought about *Ohm Krüger*. That was a propaganda film, this was the grim reality.

Only a few kilometres from a smoke-engulfed Warsaw we were driven in armoured half-tracks to a small village. It was the usual poor place, just an unpaved street of cottages with a church at one end and an inn at the other. Our commander ordered us to 'get all those swine out of their pig sties' but to be on our guard because 'these vermin will not go easily'. In the first cottage I found no one, in the second I edged in and was startled into firing off a round when what turned out to be a rat rushed across the floor in a dark corner. It set my pulse racing. In the next dwelling, when I pulled back a curtain to a wall alcove, I was shocked to find a cowering dark-haired young woman with a small child held tightly to her chest. My eyes met her haunting begging, pleading, defiant green eyes. The eyes of a 'gypsy princess'? In that second, my life changed. I knew what we were engaged in were 'evil things'. I drew the curtain into its original position and left.

Outside the few villagers who had been discovered - mainly old men, women and children - were marched off to a nearby field by two of our men. The commander drew the rest of us to attention. 'Those are bandits and the whores of bandits. They must be exterminated like vermin. Any of you who hasn't the guts to see it through for *'Führer, Volk und Fatherland'* take one pace forward,' he bellowed. With his temple visibly throbbing, he then stood and glared at us, as if we were no better than the 'vermin' we should be killing.

After what seemed like a lifetime, but was only a second or two, one of the older former policemen stepped forward. 'I am a Catholic, I can't do that. These are God's creatures too.' He had saved us. Several of us now stepped smartly forward including the two Spaniards. 'Those men fall out,' commanded the *Hauptsturmführer*. 'The rest follow me.' Minutes later we heard the sound of machine-gun fire, a few cries, isolated pistol shots and then silence. We looked at one another but said nothing. I guess we all knew what the other was thinking.

What we had been told could not happen, happened on 16 October 1944, the Red Army broke through into the German Reich. Despite our counter attacks and stubborn defensive actions, we were forced back ... and back ... and back. Occasionally, we travelled by train, sometimes by truck, but often we simply marched on foot. We slept in schools, town halls, barracks, barns, abandoned homes, burned out buildings or simply in the open. Unrealistic assessments by the German political leadership resulted in chaotic evacuations of civilians and soldiers in the wake of Soviet breakthroughs. We soon established that any fear of what the Red Army would do to civilians was well-founded. We were part of the mixed force sent to counterattack in the Gumbinnen-Insterburg area of East Prussia. We recaptured the village of Nemmersdorf which had figured prominently in Joseph Goebbel's propaganda. Sadly, we had to confirm that the horror stories were true. In the village we found a whole column of refugees – wagons, horses and people – squashed flat by the tanks of the 2nd Battalion, 25th Guards Tank Brigade, belonging to the 2nd Guards Tank Corps of the 11th Guards Army. It was horrific. Several of us just threw up. On the edge of the street an old woman had been killed by a bullet in the back of the neck. A baby had been shot at close range through the forehead. Farther along, we found a man nailed to a barn door. Near the large inn, *Weisser Krug*, we came upon a cart to which four naked women were nailed through their hands in a cruciform position. Worse was to come. In the houses we found over seventy people, including young girls and old men, all killed in a bestial manner. The stench from these houses was indescribable. We needed extra brandy that day as we cleared the corpses. One or two of our group were told to remain to give testimony to the journalists from Switzerland and Sweden.

Our local success did not last. The Russians crossed the Angrapa Bridge and we were hurled back westwards. As we fell back we saw the tragedy of East Prussia unfolding. Hundreds, thousands, tens of thousands, hundreds of thousands, sought to evade the advancing Red Army. It was utter chaos. It was a great trek of people mostly either on foot or travelling on farm carts. Many did not make it.

Thousands fell victim to the bombs or machine guns of the Soviet planes. Others found that the Soviets were ahead of them and shot them down as they arrived at the next village or town. Others were less fortunate and the women were robbed and raped before, in many cases, being shot. Sometimes we found villages, which had been put to the torch; other times we found villages intact over which a deathly silence prevailed. All inhabitants had simply fled. Once or twice we found someone haunting the village who had simply gone mad.

Even allied prisoners-of-war were not safe from the Soviets. As the Soviet troops, often from the Asian republics, could not always distinguish the uniforms or nationality of the groups they came upon, and could not believe prisoners could be in such good shape; they often preferred to shoot them to be safe and sure. We chanced upon Belgium prisoners shot in this way. But, as we already knew, the senseless cruelty against civilians, helpless prisoners and others was not all on the Red side. As we fought our rear guard actions on the road to Berlin, we discovered more Nazi insanity. In a field where we were going to rest for a while, we came upon what appeared to be seventy to hundred prisoners who had obviously been machine-gunned by their guards before they fled. They were emaciated wretches in the ragged stripped uniforms of the German concentration camps. No one would be calling the neutral press to see these victims. On other occasions, we passed other bodies in the same tattered uniforms. We concluded that they were on a forced march and had been too unwell to keep up with the column. They had, therefore, been shot. Perhaps the most horrific sight for us were members of the German armed forces hanging from lamp posts. German officers with placards around their necks proclaiming, 'I conspired with the Bolsheviks'. Apparently, they had wanted to surrender in a hopeless situation. Others were hanged bearing placards, 'I am defeatist' or 'I tried to desert'. This could have meant simply they had got cut off from their units. It was a nonsense and yet a further, senseless, waste of life. Of course, there were deserters. Morale was sinking on a daily basis, as one illusion after another was shattered. We were either on the road to hell - or already there.

Our enemy was not just the Soviets. The weather had become a deadly adversary. We were relatively well off in that our organisation was still largely intact and was being supplied, and we were a fairly privileged group within that organisation. It sounds pathetic but it is true that the enemy were better prepared for winter warfare, even though they were expected to exist on far less than we were. The winter of 1944-45 was one of the coldest in European history with temperatures regularly dipping below zero on the Fahrenheit scale. This was coupled with heavy snow falling along our line of retreat and with freezing cold and fog. Cold hurts, cold can make you go mad, cold can make you just want to give up. While sitting huddled up waiting to confront our enemy or move on, you could feel the cold taking over, doing its worst, slowing creeping up the body's extremities. I only had to remember the contorted frozen figures I'd seen to help me fight against it. I wasn't going to perish here. We suffered from all of this and our morale sank lower as we saw the suffering of the civilians we were supposed to be defending. Several times we came on the bodies of fleeing refugees who had simply died overnight attempting to rest in the open. Sometimes, refugees had lit fires only to be spotted by marauding Soviet planes prepared to attack any sign of life beyond their own advance guard. It was for that reason that we went day after day on cold rations since any kind of smoke would attract Red Army interest. Often we saw pathetic creatures, soldiers and civilians, suffering from frost-bite, hobbling along for a kilometre or two more before giving up. Usually, there was little we could do to help them. Occasionally, we frightened others to take them in their vehicles or frightened villagers into giving them temporary shelter or a hot soup. We saw acts of kindness but we also saw great selfishness among those who foolishly thought the Red Army was not coming their way. This hit our morale too.

As the winter gradually gave way to spring and we were still alive we became more optimistic. We told ourselves that the enemy would be held at this point or that - Danzig, Kolberg, Stettin - but the retreat went on. Finally, the spring had come and to our utter despair we were in the suburbs of Berlin. Surely the summer would bring a reversal of fortunes? But I guess, deep down I knew the game was up and it was now just a matter of months, perhaps even weeks. But I didn't let it show. It would now be a question of survival.

9.

The fall of Berlin

March 1945 found me in Angermünde, about 35 miles south of Stettin in what is now Poland. It was an eventful stay for two reasons. I was surprised on my second day to hear English being spoken in a variety of accents including north of England, Home Counties, cockney and South African. It turned out there was a Legion of St George after all and they had been added to SS *Nordland Panzergrenadier* Division of which I was a member. For my reasons of personal security, I decided not to confide in them that I was British myself. Most of the Danes with whom I had first served, and who knew my true identity, had disappeared long ago. They had been killed, wounded, were missing or had returned to Denmark. Over the short time I was with the Legion I got to know that they were ex-prisoners-of-war who, like me, had been impressed by Amery. There were only about ten to fifteen of them and they had seen little or no action. They claimed they had been cut off from the headquarters' staff in the west. Now they thought their big moment was at hand, defending Berlin from the Soviets. The other significant event in Angermünde was a third encounter with a Soviet bullet. This only put me out of action for a short time after which I was ordered to report back to my unit which had now moved on. I found them in a park in the Berlin suburb of Treptow in the south-east of the city.

'Sie gehören zu uns!' 'You belong with us!' this was the legendary Miguel Ezquerra, whose deeds were known far beyond the ranks of the Spanish volunteers. By April 1945, he had only three companies of Spaniards left from the Blue Division, the bulk having been killed, wounded or withdrawn by Franco under pressure from the Americans. Colonel Ezquerra commanded the remnants of the Spanish force together with French, Belgian and a few Danish SS survivors. He joked with me at first, 'I thought all you English were Reds! No seriously, I met one or two on our side in '38. They were gallant gentlemen.'

It was an honour (or so I thought then) to join Ezquerra, but by that time our dream was shattered. The long and perilous retreat over the previous 18 months had been a devastating experience. We knew only a miracle would save us. Goebbel's propaganda machine tried to lift our spirits with reports and rumours of 'revenge weapons': the V1 and V2 rockets, the new jet planes, like the Messerschmitt Me 262 *Schwalbe* (swallow) and other surprises for the enemy. He had claimed the Western Allies and the Soviets would soon fall out, yet their advance continued unchecked. There on the outskirts of Berlin, on that sunny day with the blossoming trees and the odd bird tweeting, it was easy to forget the true situation for a few moments. We had plenty of ammunition, relatively good rations with smokes and drinks, and the district of Treptow was not too badly devastated. Somehow the news that Germany's most decorated soldier, fighter pilot Hans-Ulrich Rudel, had been shot down seemed a harbinger of the end of the Third Reich. Rudel was soon followed by Hermann Graf. Both held the coveted Knight's Cross with Oak Leaves, Swords and Diamonds. If they'd been shot out of the skies what chance was there for anyone else? Miraculously, both survived the war. Our own organisation and leadership was starting to show signs of disintegration. The commander of the SS Nordland Division, General Jürgen Ziegler, was replaced by General Gustav Krukenberg because of leadership rivalries and differences of opinion. This was not a good omen. Better the devil you know…

Ezquerra saw it as a sign of our weakness. He had been forced to the conclusion that the end of the war was close. He issued me with a new service pay book indicating that my place of birth was not Guernsey but Allenstein, East Prussia. This would ensure that if I was taken prisoner my true identity would not be revealed. I noticed that he had written in my real date of birth, thus making me a year younger. He did not comment on it, nor did I. He also handed me the Iron Cross, second class, with suitable documentation and promoted me to *Unterscharführer*, roughly that of a sergeant.

Two days later Ezquerra and most of the others were on their way towards the centre of Berlin to link up with the remnants of the French SS Grenadier Division Charlemagne. They were soon in action in the adjacent district of Neuköln. Ironically many foreigners were among the last defenders of Berlin. I was ordered to stay put in command of what Ezquerra called a reconnaissance and communications group. We set ourselves up in a disused printing factory which was only lightly damaged and awaited our fate. As *Unterscharführer* I had a motley group under me. There were two Berliners old enough to be my father from a local *Volkssturm* (Home guard) unit; the *Volkssturm* was made up of the elderly, the under-age and the unfit. Naturally, they had seen no action. An unlucky Luftwaffe walla, home on leave, had been pressed into service with us. There were also two French Kameraden recovering from wounds, two Danes and one or two others. We listened on the wireless, stern faced, to Goebbels who was urging us to fight to the bitter end. What was I, a 17-year-old Englishman, doing commanding this remnant of the 'first European army' in the ruins of a disintegrating empire? Was it all a tragedy or a farce?

A curious event took place during the last days. We were entertained by other SS comrades in a brewery which was still full of the precious liquid. The slogan of the 'party' was 'Enjoy the war while you can. The peace will be terrible.' The beer flowed and flowed with everyone over-indulging and letting their inhibitions go. There were local girls in plenty and female auxiliaries from the services. Our natural appetites took over and many men and women rightly thought this would be their last chance to fulfil their sexual urges. I too through off my inhibitions and went with one and then a little later another. The next morning, when I came to with the sound of gun fire in my ears, I had a hazy recollection of shouting at a girl, 'For Christ's sake give me a blow job!' I think she obeyed the order of her superior officer.

As the days went by, the noise of gunfire got ever nearer and more intense. We were involved in little activity. We saw a platoon of Cossack scouts whom we identified as Reds rather than 'our' Cossacks, so we kept concealed until they had passed. We saw an SS 'flying court' of young fanatics with hardly a decoration among them, hunting for deserters to hang and we kept out of their way as well. Soon it became apparent that the front had passed us by. We had been cut off. On 1 May, we heard via the radio that Hitler was dead. Before we could recover from that shock, news came of the surrender by General Weidling, the Berlin commander. I released the three Germans who lost no time in getting out. I know, in one case, he suffered no further consequences as a 'defender of Berlin'. What could we foreigners do? I left each man to make his own decision. The Danes, not much older than me, took their chance and I never saw or heard of them again. Perhaps they reached neutral Sweden, perhaps not. I felt my best chance was to link up with a larger group of the German forces capitulating on that day. My instinct proved right and I found myself in Pankow, a district to the north of the Berlin, with a mixed group of Wehrmacht, SS, and *Volkssturm* under the command of an army major. We sat silently, some smoking, others just in a day dream amongst the rubble, wondering what our fate was to be. We were sick with worry as we awaited the victorious Red Army.

10.

In Soviet hands

During the months that followed the Berlin surrender I was to ask myself a thousand times over why I had not followed my Danish comrades' example and tried to escape to neutral Sweden. Whether it was because I felt I should share the fate of my adopted homeland, whether it was because I thought it was safer, with the war still on, to be anonymous in a fairly large group of fellow prisoners, whether it was the belief that considering what I had been through it could not be all that bad in Soviet hands, or whether it was simply inertia, I do not know. I do know that life became hell. The individual acts of wanton cruelty we saw were mainly directly against civilians. But I saw one which occurred in our 'camp'. A sailor who protested against having his wedding ring as well as his watch 'liberated' by a Red Army soldier was simply shot dead through the forehead. His brains splattered all over those in a 15ft radius. Had he not got home compassionate leave from the naval base at Kiel, he would not have been drafted into the *Volkssturm* and would not have ended up with us. How senseless life can be! Such acts were relatively rare in the 'camp'. We suffered far more from the disorganised state of the Red Army. Many of the troops we encountered were Asians, who were poorly equipped, badly clothed and looked poor physical specimens. Their transport was largely carts drawn by mules and occasionally ponies, plus a few American trucks and captured German vehicles. They had been expected to live off the land. Capture by such a horde was a totally demoralising experience. The other demoralising experience was the fact that so many of the other Wehrmacht prisoners didn't want to associate with members of the dreaded SS. It appeared that most of the *Kameradenschaft* (comradeship) which had been a fundamental tenet of the doctrine of the German armed forces had evaporated.

We were simply herded together in the remains of a wrecked factory and left for days without any provisions whatsoever. Luckily, one or two taps were still providing water and bits of debris were used to boil it. The only food available was that which you could beg, borrow or steal. Once or twice Berliners threw some food over the fence. I felt really terrible and found myself, for the first time in years, thinking about Mr Spencer and his experience eating roast rat as prisoner in 1917. That both raised my spirits and made me feel that I had been a fool. Had I missed Amery's visit to our internment camp that afternoon in 1942 I'd probably already be on my way home. In my desperation I thought of revealing my true identity and then I thought better of it. Even if the Soviets took my claim seriously, the British could hang me as a traitor. I was trapped.

After a few more days in our first 'camp' we joined a larger group and were marched eastwards, thinning out on the way, through deaths and desertions. It appeared that occasionally a prisoner did manage to escape. Those who fell by the wayside were stripped of their footwear and any other valuables and tossed into an open truck. We stopped in makeshift camps sometimes for days on end. Delays could be disastrous because this meant we got even less food. Normally, we were fed meagre rations from ex-German army field kitchens. At one stage we were put to work in beet fields or on other crops. This at least enabled us to take the risk and steal some extra food - though if caught the consequences were brutal. On our way through Poland we were jeered at, spat at and stoned. Any remaining dignity we had was rapidly crumbling. The last stage of our journey was by goods train and then another forced march to a proper camp near Moscow. There they put us to work. The work was forestry. It was heavy manual work with primitive tools. It seemed incredible that the state which had produced the T-34 tank and other weapons of similar quality should waste manpower like this. One of the few advantages of the work was that most of the day we were outside the camp. Some of the more enterprising comrades caught animals in the forest, others of an entrepreneurial frame of mind traded occasionally with the local peasants and prisoners from other armies. We had felt that we were poor until we met the locals. Although free, they were very poor compared to what we had seen even in Poland. Seeing the reality of Soviet Russia, even allowing for the war devastation and we were in a part never occupied by the Wehrmacht, we could not understand how the system had survived since 1917 and triumphed in 1945.

I had neither skills as a hunter nor skills as a trader, but to my surprise, my native tongue came to my rescue. In our hut was Klaus, a man aged 27, that is, ten years my senior. By profession he was a teacher of French and English, but never having been to England, nor having had much time to practise his profession, his English was poor. 'Only had some old Jew as a teacher,' was his excuse. I could not help joking with him in English in an unguarded moment. He soon found my knowledge of the language was far greater than his. I had to invent English relatives on my mother's side and several visits to the country. He was mollified by this explanation, otherwise he would have hated me, a mere uneducated lad knowing his subject better than he did. He took me under his wing. He was a hunter. He had gained all the proficiency badges for field craft available in the Hitler Youth. Now he put his skills to good use. He also admired me to a degree because of my Waffen SS service; he had 'only' served in the army artillery. Fortunately for me, our ranks had been similar with his being one higher than mine, *Unterfeldwebel*, staff sergeant as against my sergeant's rank. One other gain from my friendship with Klaus was our common interest in Russian. Being a teacher of languages, he had been selected to learn the language as part of his military training. Now his practical knowledge of it was rapidly improving. By 1945, I had just got used to learning the language of the people around me - German, Danish, Spanish and Russian. Klaus enjoyed putting his teaching skills to use and felt he was repaying me for what he considered my far more useful offering of English. His friendship, food and protection probably kept me out of serious misfortune until the summer of 1945. Then misfortune turned into a blessing. One day in the stifling heat of a Russian summer I collapsed.

Dr Galina Katz wore an ill-fitting white blouse, probably home-made, and a drab skirt under her open medical robe. Her dark hair already revealed a hint of grey; her brown eyes seemed to focus on another time, another place rather than the bare hut which served as an isolation ward. She was, nonetheless, quite arousing - particularly when I caught a glimpse of her cleavage through the gap of that tight blouse. It set my pulse sky high. 'You had a fever,' she said quietly in German, 'but you're over the worst.' She checked my temperature and, apparently satisfied, moved on to the next patient. I blushed slightly and hoped she hadn't noticed the palpitations.

There were several of us in the tiny, somewhat stuffy hut. Our normal 'nurse' was Hans, who had been a medical orderly in the Luftwaffe. I learnt compassion from him, to the extent that he took good care of us whatever branch of the armed forces we had been in without fear or favour. The encounter was fruitful. I subsequently found out that he was 'gay' and meeting him helped me to revise my previous extreme antipathy for homosexuals, which was the product of my indoctrination from school onwards.

Dr Katz returned some days later still with her ill-fitting blouse. She seemed much happier and engaged me in a brisk but short, though not unfriendly, conversation. Afterwards, I felt strangely aroused again but couldn't relieve myself due to the proximity of others. I looked forward to her visits with relish. On perhaps her fourth visit she asked if I was really German. I told her what I had told Klaus. That seemed to satisfy her. I then went over to the offensive. 'Are you really Russian?' 'I am Jewish, German-Jewish. My mother is Russian,' she said firmly. Her Communist parents had left Germany for Moscow in 1933. On her next visit, by which time I was the sole occupant of the hut, she asked me if I would like to get out of forestry and do some translating instead. It was like a miracle. I could not believe my ears. I readily agreed and was advised to say nothing to anyone else until the day of departure. I was discharged a couple of days later.

Within a week I was called to the camp administration office and told I was being transferred. As requested, I only told Klaus on the day of my departure. He was dismayed and somewhat hurt when I evaded the issue of where and why I was leaving. 'I don't know exactly. I only know that

I've been ordered to go. Thanks for everything. I hope we meet again in the *Heimat*.' Returning to the *Heimat* or homeland was what kept the prisoners going. I was no longer sure where *Heimat*, physically or spiritually, was or where I was going. Without realising it I was embarking on a new stage of my life.

11.

My Jewish friends

I collected my meagre belongings such as they were and left the camp with two others. One, it was rumoured, had worked as a technician on rockets in Peenemünde, the other, it was thought, had been a member of the German Communist Party before Hitler took over in 1933. We climbed aboard a covered US truck, which had benches in it, with a Soviet guard. We travelled in silence. At the local railway station our documents were checked by uniformed Ministry of Interior officers and we were told to report, on arrival in Moscow, to the station security office. We embarked the crowded train and were under way. Again we travelled in silence. From my point of view I just wanted to digest the change of scenery with its new sights and sounds. After only brief comments about the whereabouts of the security office, which we found without difficulty, we found the courage to say '*Alles Gute!*', 'All the best!' to each other and entered.

A ferocious looking official took down our particulars and then handed the other two to a man in civilian clothes. I never saw either of them again. I was left sitting on a bench for what seemed an eternity until an Interior Ministry soldier ordered me to follow him to an awaiting black car. We drove at great speed to the outskirts of Moscow through what must have been a middle class suburb before the revolution. The overall impression was one of drabness and neglect, of a fine inheritance. It was autumn 1945. The car stopped sharply outside a compound with a high, rusting, metal fence and the driver simply indicated this was where I was to alight and report.

The ornate, old iron gate clanged shut behind me and I entered the compound with some trepidation. I'd been ordered to report to a large pre-Revolutionary mansion in its own grounds. After the usual preliminaries with the security guard, examination of papers, then on to the office for further examination and phone calls, I was escorted in silence to a small modern building in the grounds. My guide ushered me into a light, medium-sized office over-flowing with books, manuals, files, papers and the obligatory thick smoke given off by the distinctive smelling Russian cigarettes. Utter chaos reigned. Stalin looked down from every side. It reminded me of my first impressions of Breslau's HQ. It did seem a dim and distant memory although barely two years had elapsed. I smiled inwardly with a feeling of déjà-vu. There was Stalin the military strategist in Marshal's uniform, Stalin making a point as he walked with Molotov, Stalin advising workers on some problem and 'Uncle Joe' Stalin, the friend of children. What did Lenin think? He looked on shrewdly from a corner. Upon checking my documents for the umpteenth time, a small, round, ungainly little man, almost bald and wearing steel-rimmed spectacles welcomed me.

'Blumenkohl' he said extending his hand and introducing himself. After a few preliminary greetings and a few brief questions in Russian, Kurt Blumenkohl spoke to me in German for about ten minutes. He tested my political outlook. I don't remember what I said exactly but I was confused and knew I had to be careful with my responses. He then switched to English. This is where I scored. He spoke with a very strong German accent and his grammar was poor. He believed I would be an asset to the department and made appropriate moves to secure my services on 'important party work'. This was translating the statements of the Soviet government and mass organisations into English and German. It was not as daunting as I first thought it would be. The same words, phrases, jargon, even sentences came up again and again. Kurt always checked the finished translation and I could go to him if, because of my initial limited Russian and ideological training, I could not quite understand the line of argument. As far as English publications were concerned, we could read the London *Daily Worker* and the Soviet Weekly. These were invaluable to me because I could learn the correct political vocabulary for my work. I also started to get a few ideas from the *Daily Worker*, which was, after all, written for a readership in a democratic country. I also saw *Neues Deutschland* from East Berlin.

Always a great enthusiast, Kurt got me to work immediately. I was put in a room with several others who were not introduced at that stage, and given a text on Soviet trade union democracy to translate into German. After about two hours, Kurt came and took me to sit with him in a small dining room. Over soup and bread he asked more questions about me and my experiences, interrupting to speak rapidly about various historical and political questions in a mixture of German and Russian. I learned to keep away from Kurt at lunch times for I was 'shelled' or was it 'machine-gunned' by his food throughout the meal. He seemed to take a shine to me. I think it was because his own son had been killed in the war, and because he saw in me a chance to convert, salvage and win over a misguided German working boy. Of course, he didn't know that I wasn't German and I didn't emphasise that I was not working class. A Jewish, German-speaking Communist from the Sudetenland, he had been in the Soviet Union since the fall of Prague in 1939. Kurt was a fanatic with a desire to proselytise. In me he had found the perfect target. To me he was kind and considerate and showed patience with my ideological and translation errors. Intellectual though he was, Kurt liked to play the German card game *Skat*. The only card game I had ever learned was whist; my mother loved to play. I often wondered how she was and lamented my lack of contact over the years. Despite my shortcomings at cards, we both enjoyed chess and occasionally played in his office. I was to learn that, compared to most people in Moscow in the summer of 1946, Kurt was very relaxed and frequently broke the rules of security.

I was given accommodation within the compound where I shared a small room with three others. They turned out to be translators into French, Italian and Spanish. They were members of Communist families who sought refuge in the Soviet Union before the war. We were issued with books of vouchers for our meals. We also received pocket money which we needed to buy elementary toiletry items from the canteen shop. In theory, we had freedom of movement within the compound grounds and in the local suburb. Very security conscious, my room mates said little about themselves. Their faces, however, could not conceal that they had known tragedy and hardship. Enrique, a tall gangling, tubercular-looking Spaniard of around twenty five was in charge of our room and was expected to keep an eye on us, our movements, friendships, political comments and so on. It was rumoured that his father, a professor, and mother, had been shot by the Francoists in Spain. He was one of a group of orphans who had been sent to the Soviet Union and who left there in the 1950s. As one would expect, I was uneasy because I did not know quite what my companions had been told about me. My protection, unknown to me at the time, was that the Soviet, and therefore the German, Communist line was that German youngsters whatever their background should be won for the cause of Socialism. I had been picked out as a potential recruit.

One day Kurt came into the office happily humming a tune. 'My word, you sound happy,' I remarked, in an effort to keep the mood upbeat.

'Yes, I've just heard that a close friend of mine has survived Theresienstadt concentration camp and is now back in Prague.'

'I'm very pleased for you,' I responded. 'But what's the tune?' I asked, slightly embarrassed at the mention of concentration camps.

'The tune! The tune! Surely you recognise The International?'

Of course, I had never heard of it? Why should I have done? Later that week Kurt brought me the Red Worker's Song Book, apologising that he had only got the English version. He also gave me some clothing, which although worn and slightly too big, was a great improvement on what I had and I heartily thanked him. Later, alone in the room I studied the song, '…the International unites the human race.' I broke down and wept. I had been brought up on Land of Hope and Glory and tales of the British Empire. Where did that lead? Then came *Deutschland über Alles* and the Nazi party anthem *Horst Wessel Lied* also known as *Die Fahne hoch*. Where had they led Germany and me? They were three good tunes with poor texts. I had come to realise there were good (and bad) people in all countries. The International was a good tune too and the words sounded like common sense, '...unites the human race.' I read them over and over. I realised that was what my emotions had always yearned for and what the world needed.

After about a week working for Kurt he brought me a note which he gave to me in a furtive manner. It was from Dr Galina Katz. I got excited and my heart rate increased as it had done in the hut. Would I like to spend an afternoon at the weekend in the local park with her? She gave me the time and the place. All I had to do was indicate to Kurt that I was available. Clearly, I was available and I was grateful for the offer. We met on several Sundays in this way until one day she invited me to her flat on Tchaikovsky St not so far from the park.

Her flat was in a mansion from the period before the 1914-18 war. The house had been divided up into flats after the revolution. She had two rooms, something of a luxury, but shared a lavatory and bathroom with several other occupants. The sink in one of her rooms and a two-ring electric hot plate were great luxuries. The massive book case and the parquet floor were part of the original fittings and the large dining table, half covered in books, pamphlets and documents, had belonged to the pre-Revolutionary owners. The large couch was almost certainly from that period. Who knew what expressions of hope, fear, sadness and joy it had been witness to? There were one or two rugs from Azerbaijan. The large walls were bare except for a Russian landscape, a portrait of

Lenin and a poster for an Eisenstein film. She had a 1930s German gramophone on which she played Shostakovich, Tchaikovsky and - quite a treat in Moscow then - Rachmaninov records. I could not help making comparisons between Frau Hilde, her home and way of life, and Galina's much shabbier home and much harder life. The age gap between them was not great. Of course, I did not even know whether Hilde was still alive. I had received three postcards from her before July 1944 but nothing after. Had she survived the bombing, siege and capture of Königsberg? I felt and certainly hoped, she would have seen the writing on the wall and got out in good time. On the other hand, bombs and bullets were indiscriminate. Once again, I also thought of my mother. Would she now be home in Guernsey? What would she find there? What would she say about me? With her greying black hair and dark eyes Galina reminded me slightly of her.

My visits to Galina started to become a regular weekend event and she tried her best to provide us with a meal, severely limited though she was in terms of facilities and the extremely poor variety of foods available in Moscow at that time. Once I got to know the Soviet Union better, I realised what effort she must have put into those meals. On one occasion, which was to become significant, she produced a yoghurt, cucumber and herbs dish, canned sardines, mashed potato, washed down with a fruity Azerbaijan red wine. She proceeded to tell me more about her family.

As it turned out, Galina was the niece of Kurt, otherwise we could not have had private contact with each other and I would not have got the job in the first place. She was the daughter of an Austrian Communist medical practitioner and a Russian mother. The mother, whom I never met, was said to be on party work elsewhere, but officially still lived with Galina, which explained the size of the apartment. Her father had died in Stalin's purges of 'Rightists and Trotskyists' at the end of the 1930s. Her uncle Kurt, whom she greatly admired, had arrived after the purges had ended. One day when she was trying to explain the family situation she burst out, 'Yes, some terrible things have been done, and some bad mistakes made, but once Stalin knows about these things he will deal with the culprits. He had those criminal double-dealers Yagoda and Yezhov shot in 1938! Our state covers one sixth of the entire world's surface. Just think about that! How can Stalin know what's going on everywhere?' Her dark eyes flashed with passion. (Later I learned that both 'double-dealers' had been heads of the secret police and purged at the same time as her father.) I could not suppress a smile, 'Was the letter 'Y' unlucky in Russia?' I asked myself. Also, she looked wonderful when she lit up with passion. I was almost spellbound and she certainly aroused me.

'Why are you smiling?' she enquired.

'You look wonderful when you get on your soap box,' I could not help replying.

'Oh you, be serious.'

'I'm very serious, but you, your beauty, the sun, I admit, the wine, I can't help it.'

She blushed. We looked at each other for an instance. She searched my face and then we started kissing. After some hugging I slid my hand under her skirt and was offered no resistance. The warmth coming from between her legs told me that she felt just as passionate about me. We tore off each other's clothes and rolled and writhed around with excitement first on the couch, then the floor and finally on the bed. For a few hours we forgot the class war and our parts on opposite sides of the barricades.

12.

We German anti-fascists

I did not particularly take to Colonel Heinz Fischer, holder of the Knight's Cross and many other decorations received for his services in Hitler's Wehrmacht. He had a rather mean face and cold eyes behind his steel-rimmed glasses. After his capture by the Red Army in 1943, he had helped to found the National Committee for a Free Germany (NKFD). The aim was to undermine the Nazi-led German armed forces and overthrow Hitler and his gang. Field Marshal Paulus, who had surrendered at Stalingrad, later lent his support without becoming prominent in the organisation. Although the NKFD had been dissolved in 1945, the Soviets were active in converting the German POWs. I had been invited to a conference, held in a former monastery near Moscow, to meet both Wehrmacht veterans like myself and German Communists like Kurt and Galina (who was not, however, present). Fischer was one of the main speakers and told us that the aim of the Soviet Union was to create a united, democratic, anti-fascist German which would never again be a threat to its neighbours. Who could quarrel with such an aim? Kurt and I applauded as enthusiastically as the rest. Wilhelm Adam, who had been with Paulus at Stalingrad, was also there. There were a number of writers, some of whom had been flown from Germany for the occasion. Most of their names I have long since forgotten. Many were not very prominent in the literary world and just faded away later. Within a year or two, however, some had left to live in West Germany. Among those I do recall was Ludwig Renn, the aristocrat and former Kaiser's officer who became a Communist. He had written a well-known book Krieg (War), which I was to read later. Theodor Plievier was another I remember because I thought his book Stalingrad was a realistic portrayal of the war on the eastern front. He too later defected to West Germany and then went to Switzerland where he died not long after. There was also Erich Weinert, the well-known Communist poet. Among the guests were a small group of former Hitler Youth functionaries who a short time later were to help Erich Honecker found the Free German Youth. Our Soviet hosts, somewhat tight-lipped and anxious, kept in the background.

Our speaker told us of the terrible conditions prevailing in Germany resulting from Hitler's determination to fight to the end and that Germany would have to make good what it had destroyed or plundered in other countries. More importantly, we were told that the new Germany needed all its sons and daughters and that there were going to be many opportunities for those who had learned from past mistakes. During the excellent buffet lunch following Fischer's speech, Kurt steered me in his direction. Even before Kurt introduced me, I could see the Colonel had a rough idea, from my bearing as well as my age, of my background. Before Kurt could open his mouth he asked, '*Sie haben gedient?*' ('You've served?') '*In welcher Einheit?*' ('In which unit?') Instinctively drawing myself attention, I told him, '*Waffen SS, Herr Oberst.*' His glass shook slightly and he blinked. 'So,' he said, 'And now you're in the circle of friends of the Soviet Union. Very good!'

When I told him what I was doing now, translation work with Kurt, he seemed impressed and could not quite suppress a smile. I felt he was thinking, 'God, he must be almost as smart as I am. From the SS to a cushy office job in Moscow in just under a year.' We talked in vague generalities for a few minutes before one of his aides (or minders) politely moved him on.

For Kurt, I was a kind of parade horse, the one he had saved. He meant well and I always remained grateful to him. He taught me a great deal. One person he did not steer me towards was a ravishing creature just several feet away with copper hair and honey-coloured eyes. She rivalled Hilde for style. I could not believe she was a Soviet person and yet she did not look German. She was both tastefully and expensively dressed. Slender and slightly above average height for a woman, she also appeared intelligent

She was decisively feminine, small boned, and yet infinitely strong. Her self-confidence revealed that she was clearly at home in such gatherings. She was quite glamorous, but not in the way of an actress. A professor? No, too glamorous and too young for that profession though I had not yet met a lady professor. A writer perhaps? I wanted to break away from Kurt and edge towards her but I dared not. He was, after all, Galina's uncle and I had no idea what he thought about sexual infidelity, marriage and so on. I estimated he would be jealous in his niece's interest. In any case, I had no idea what she would have thought of me. At that moment the tall, blond rather sad-looking, Major Egbert von Frankenberg, the German fighter ace and SS member, who had defected to the Soviets, was in the circle of admirers. Like many men, he looked older than his years, but the handsome Major also looked strangely uneasy. He turned away and, glancing in my direction, looked startled then puzzled. Meanwhile, she was giving her attention to an elderly, white-haired Soviet composer. Was she emphasising her intellectual, spiritual side? Was she making a display of her humanity and respect for her elders? Or was she showing all young would-be admirers that mere looks were not enough, and that they would have to work hard to gain her favours? She must have had half of Moscow at her feet, that is, if she was a resident there. Seeing this adorable creature made me realise that, although I liked and admired Galina very much and enjoyed the sex, I was not in love with her. Galina, Galina, how unfair life is! I yearned to be head over heels in love. I

101

was nearly 20, looked slightly older too, but felt middle-aged, and I'd never been in love. I felt certain this woman had made at least several men feel that way. After my encounter with her, which was no encounter at all, I became more aware of the dullness of my surroundings.

The conference was the first of many in the Soviet Union I was to attend over the following six months. They consisted of long-winded, boring lectures followed by good lunches and a plentiful supply of alcohol, Soviet cigarettes and cigars. As I was to find out, given the shortages in Moscow and Berlin, the lunches and other meals were very tempting and I was not surprised to find some people were regular attendees like myself.

At the conference little was said in detail about Nazi crimes, but as the details were made known I felt really guilty and really sick. I had been criminally stupid and was a very lucky man. I shuddered to think how close I must have been to being drawn into the worst type of war crimes. Thank God, at least I followed the Catholic police inspector and said 'No' on that terrible occasion in Poland. When the details of Auschwitz were revealed I felt really bad. Such madness! Such evil! To think that people like Kurt and Galina could have been murdered, not as political opponents, which is unacceptable anyway, but just because of their ethnic origins. And all those talented individuals who had no politics, who could have helped Germany; this was political, economic and strategic folly and lunacy, as well as being plain evil. Who had known about it? I could say with a clear conscience, we, that is, the men in my unit, did not. What about the higher officers? What about the Colonel? Surely they must have known! Surely something of this magnitude could not have had so few witnesses. Müller and the Colonel denied that they had known about Auschwitz specifically, but admitted they had known about other Nazi crimes and deeply regretted their parts in them.

The conference and others like it stressed the importance of nations and the national question. Stalin, we were informed, had said, 'Hitlers come and go, but the German state and the German people go on forever.' The propaganda line was that each country would develop according to its own traditions; there was a 'German road to Socialism'. Kurt's humming of The International was, in a sense, slightly deviant. Far more often we heard the song, 'Soviet Land so dear to every toiler. Peace and Progress pin their hopes on thee.' The Soviet's German friends were expected to win converts for the German national cause. This too seemed attractive, but not quite so attractive as The International uniting the whole human race. Or was I just being too idealistic?

13.

Alexandra Chekov

The book I'm sure was called, Far from Moscow, the author's name I just don't remember. I do know it was to be translated into English, French, German and several other languages. At the conference, at which the author spoke, Soviet patriotism and internationalism, 'two sides of the same coin', were on the menu. After so many conferences, at which I had learned a great deal, I realised I needed to take a crash course in the Marxist classics - Marx, Engels, Lenin and Stalin - particularly the last two, who always seemed to be quoted. Andrei Zhadanov was cropping up more and more too. Who was he? I have to admit, there was so much jargon to learn and I was getting weary. I was developing a learning and conference fatigue. I was rather bored. This was reflected by my rising alcohol consumption.

As I was on perhaps my third or fourth glass of Soviet champagne, just before the end, and was, as usual, standing alone. She came through the door majestically. She was like a bee; she was soon surrounded by several older men with many younger ones just looking on. I just stared at her half dazed.

'Hello', she said smiling and showing her sparkling white teeth. She was actually speaking to me.

'Hello', I replied. 'Are we speaking English?' I asked myself.

'I'm Alexandra Chekov, aged 23 and Russian.' She spoke in immaculate Home Counties English. She looked at me urging me to speak.

'I'm Martin Thomas, I'm German and I'm 21.'

'Why are you lying?' she responded.

'Lying?' I nearly died. I certainly turned deep red. What did she know about me?

'You're a reformed Nazi and you're 20. Kurt has told me all about you.'

Slightly relieved and perhaps slightly flustered, I said, 'You're right! Come to think of it, I am still only 20. But I've never been a Nazi.'

'How do you come to speak such good English?' she quizzed.

'Well…on my mother's side…she has English relatives. I visited them several times. And you?'

Ignoring my question, she continued, 'Would you like a coffee?' At that moment coffee was the most wonderful drink in the world. 'I'd love one.' I followed her out of the hall into a waiting black car. The driver opened the door and she mumbled something to him that I could not catch. He obviously knew the way. After a few minutes we arrived at a Czarist palace. It was a slightly faded but still sumptuous building in extensive, well-kept grounds. Inside was a wide staircase, like the one in Scarlet O'Hara's mansion in *Gone with the Wind*, the windows were adorned with rich heavy satin curtains, there were some magnificent chandeliers and the rooms heaved with pre-Revolutionary furniture. It was the Writers' Club. She was obviously a member. One or two members greeted her.

'Are you a writer? I enquired.

'Well, I suppose I am. I have written a few short stories. He wasn't my grandfather…you know…Anton Chekov…'

Who's he? I thought. '…he was my father's cousin.' She continued rapidly. 'I'm more of an editor of English-language publications like *New Times* and *Soviet Literature*.'

'It sounds impressive.' I was impressed. She ordered coffee from a buxom waitress in a black dress and white, lace-trimmed apron, who flashed a knowing glance my way. I had no idea what it meant though.

'It isn't. I do most of the work, but someone else is the official editor. I've been able to help some of the authors a little.'

'You sound so very English,' I commented.

'It's simple.' She confided, 'My father was posted to London in 1941. I had already learned English here at a special school and I went to a very special school over there, first in Highgate, north London, and later in a Gloucester village for a year. I then returned to the Soviet Union and studied at Moscow University where I still am officially. By the way, here in Moscow we don't ask people too much about their backgrounds. It's not considered polite.'

'I apologise, I was just so impressed.' There was a brief pause. 'You know, I saw you some time ago when Colonel Fischer was here. You looked wonderful in a long dress...' She frowned, 'Which one was that then?...Ah yes, I know...Oh that old thing. If you like it so much you can have it. You'd look nice in a dress.'

I'm sure I blushed again. Looking quite stern she continued, 'Actually, I wanted to ask you about something else...' Oh, here it comes I thought. I had wondered why she'd asked me of all the people at the conference for a coffee. '...Would you be interested in working on our English or German editions?

'That would be great!' I spluttered, unable to hide my enthusiasm.

'Well, as I said before, your boss Kurt has told my boss all about you and he asked me to have a word with you about it.'

'And I thought it was because of my blue, blue eyes,' I tried to joke. It fell flat. She ignored this and indicated she had to go. I had not even had chance to finish my coffee but duly followed.

We drove back again towards the centre. As we drove, I started to have anxiety in my stomach; it was like being on the big dipper. I too-ed and fro-ed as to whether I should dare to ask her out. She was, after all, the woman of my dreams. It was torture. As the car pulled up outside the

Metro I made a snap decision and without thinking, I spluttered out, a little lamely, 'I'd like to see you again.'

'Well, if you come and work for us, we'll see much more of each other,' she replied impassively. With that the car door was shut and the car was gone. It disappeared at speed up the wide boulevard-style street. Should I have approached it differently? Questions, questions, but there were no answers. Somewhat deflated, I joined the crowds of jostling office workers heading for home.

14.

The German People's Police

I really did not know what to think as our American twin-engine DC-3, now bearing the colours of the Red Air Force, came to a bumpy halt on Schönefeld air field on the outskirts of East Berlin. Within less than a week my life had been transformed once again. To my utter disappointment, my job with Alexandra had finished before it was started. 'Higher authority' had decided I was wanted back in the Soviet Zone of Germany to serve in the German People's Police which was now being formed. I had not really had a choice. But at least I was returning to Germany as a free man. I barely found the time to say my good-byes. I was told to say nothing about my departure to my colleagues and I observed that rule of security. Kurt wished me well and gave me a bear bug; Galina was tearful and gave me one of her Shostakovich records. We kissed and looked into each other's eyes; no words were needed. We promised to write realising that we would probably never meet again. She had become a Soviet citizen and could never leave unless a German anti-Fascist organisation made a very strong case for her return to Germany.

Most of the twenty or so passengers on board the plane were Soviet officers with a few diplomats, scientists and cultural representatives. The small group of Germans were put together and ignored by their Soviet counterparts. I saw a writer, whom I had met once or twice, but he acted as if he did not recognise me. All the other Germans were making the same journey as I was. Most of us had exchanged one ideology for another and all of us one uniform for another. They all appeared very fit and I discovered that they had been in a training camp for several months prior to departure. I was again the odd one out. We were not yet clear how lucky we were. Most of our comrades, including declared anti-Fascists, had to wait a while longer before being released.

Although I enjoyed being airborne again after so many years, I was shocked by the towns we flew over. Somehow seeing the remains of the carnage from above, with no bombs or shells exploding was worse than seeing it during a battle. We spotted a few trucks and other vehicles on the road to, and in, Berlin, but the overall impression was ghostly. Perhaps it was harder for those among us who, unlike me, had known pre-war Berlin. One of our comrades, who was a Berliner and had been captive since 1941, openly wept. It was indeed a sad sight.

A Red Army covered Ford truck with benches in the back was waiting for us and an older man, who had clearly been a Wehrmacht NCO, got us to fall in and checked off the names. As we were all present we boarded the lorry without any ceremony. A Red Army jeep, another gift from the US, led the way. Its passengers, a Soviet officer and a German in civvies, were our minders.

After a drive of about 30 minutes we arrived at a former Wehrmacht barracks south east of Berlin. Most of it was occupied by the Red Army. We had our own quarters within the compound. Our living conditions in terms of accommodation and facilities were slightly below what I had experienced in Breslau in 1943. Given the situation in Germany in the autumn of 1946 the food was very good. We were provided with three hot meals a day and always with meat or fish. Many ex-servicemen, living in bombed-out ruins without heating or electricity, uncertain of their future, would have joined up just for the food, clean beds, cigarette ration, and constant supply of laundered clothes and, of course, beer money. It was also a blessing to see German women again who served the food and carried out domestic duties. Some of my comrades lost no time relieving themselves with these female anti-fascists and, in due course, some of the first generation of the future German Democratic Republic were born.

The man who had greeted us at the airport handed us over to another similar sort of person, this time in uniform. He ordered us to follow him. 'Let's get you out of those rags,' he sneered. I looked at my comrades. Yes, we were very shabbily attired. Within the hour we were in uniform again. It was basically the ordinary German Army uniform dyed dark blue with a khaki shirt and tie. We were ordered to fall in and take an oath requiring us to protect the anti-Fascist, democratic order, give unqualified obedience to our superior officers, and maintain secrecy about every aspect of our work. Before the swearing-in ceremony two officers in uniform appeared. One of them, Erich Reschke, a pre-Hitler Communist, gave a short address about the German People's Police, which he had helped to set up on 1 July 1945. We, he told us, were to be part of the German Frontier Police (DGP) which was to be set up. After the oath-taking the two officers reviewed us.

'*Wir kennen uns doch*,' (We know each other don't we?). It was Colonel Heinz Fischer who stopped in front of me on our first parade. He explained to Reschke that we had met in Moscow, at an anti-Fascist conference, a location which seemed to impress the old Communist. 'I think he'll do fine,' Fischer said to his superior officer. Later that day, I was called to the Cadres Department where a fierce-looking forty-plus comrade told me my rank would be that of senior NCO. 'You'll be wanting to join the Party I suppose?' Immediately sensing that my future depended on this, I answered in the affirmative.

For the first evening in barracks a celebratory social get together was laid on. This involved heavy drinking. Our only discomfort was not knowing, which of the old songs could be sung and which could not in the new Germany. Early next morning, and it did seem remarkably early, there was a banging and stamping at the entrance to our quarters, 'God, what a filthy, stink!' bellowed the sergeant. And then he gave us that old, military command, 'Hands off cocks, hands on socks, you filthy bastards.' Some of my comrades smiled and chuckled; they knew they were home at last.

Usually accompanied by a Soviet liaison officer, we were given intensive training over the next few summer weeks. Our marching and parading standards were refreshed. We were given 98k carbines, made by Steyr Daimler Puch from captured Wehrmacht stocks, and put through our paces at the shooting range. In this area I turned out to be the odd man out in a positive sense. I was the best shot in my unit having had much more practice, and recent practice at that, than the others. In addition, we underwent a heavy programme of ideological training covering the history of the working class movement, German and world imperialism, basic Marxist philosophy and Stalin's book, On the Roots of Leninism and the Problems of Leninism. The current situation in Germany was explained by a series of outside speakers including Walter Ulbricht and Anton Ackermann, leading members of the Socialist Unity Party (SED), Ludwig Renn and one or two others. Paul Markgraf, a former Wehrmacht captain who had been appointed police chief of Berlin, came to us to talk about the situation in Berlin. There were SED meetings once a month as well. I was immediately accepted as a candidate member together with most of my ex-Wehrmacht comrades. We were among its early members as it had only been set up in the previous April.

By November 1946, we were deployed along the inter-zonal demarcation line between the Soviet Zone and the British and American Zones which bordered it. At that time we officially came into existence; a force of 3,000. Our main tasks were to stop contraband, smuggling and black marketeering, keep our eyes open for individuals on the wanted lists, prevent sabotage of the people's property, arrest infiltrators and prevent the importation of Nazi and revanchist literature.

I remained in the DGP until the summer of 1948. In the meantime, partly due to the expansion, I was promoted to a commissioned rank. At that time, the head of the cadres department told me I was a very lucky young man. Comrade Colonel Heinz Fischer had asked for me to be sent to work for him. 'Subject to the usual security checks, of course,' he said looking gravely at me. I don't know how I looked, probably anxious, he went on, 'Yes, of course, just because some fucking Nazi wants you as his sidekick, that doesn't mean he'll get you. We determine who goes where and who does what in this fucking army.' It was the first time I'd heard the term 'army' used. Although I did not care much for Fischer personally, I was glad of the change and the prospect of more interesting work. I was tired of the barrack room life, the camaraderie of the mutual boredom, the beer bottle and the brothel, the daily routine and the lack of the intellectual companionship I had experienced in Moscow. That now seemed like a long lost golden age, as did my brief encounter with Hilde.

About two weeks after my interview with the head of the cadres department I was told to collect my belongings and report to a Berlin office, where Comrade Mielke of the Committee for the Protection of the Economy was to be found. All nations, all peoples, all ethnic groups, produce their heroic types; Erich Mielke was no such specimen. He was an ugly, short, stocky figure, with piggy eyes and a short, military-style hair cut. He was 41 years old and climbing up the security ladder fast. None of this I knew at the time. He received me politely, asking me to take a seat. On his desk he had but a few papers and they all seemed to be related to me, including the long questionnaire we had been required to fill in 'answering every question,' when we joined the People's Police.

'I understand you want to work for Fischer?' he started. I explained that I'd been asked for. 'Why should a fucking Fascist Hitlerite Colonel want you, an SS lad?' he shrieked. Totally unnerved, I tried to keep calm. I repeated my explanation and told him how we had met.

'And who introduced you to him?' he continued.

'Kurt Blumenkohl, Comrade,' I replied thinking this would satisfy.

'That bloody Trotskyite, Jewboy,' he stormed. 'My word you do keep some good company!' he sniggered.

Shaken further, I said I thought Kurt was a loyal and committed Communist. 'You were bedding the fucking niece weren't you?' he said angrily.

I replied we were good friends and that she too was a loyal Communist. 'Her father shot as a traitor, her mother in a labour camp, some loyal family!' I didn't know anything about the mother. 'And another thing,' he went on, 'Do you run after boys as well? Are you a fucking fairy?'

'Certainly not, comrade!' I responded decisively.

'Well, you've not been with any of our Berlin working class girls since you've been here. What the fuck have you been doing with yourself, Thomas?' he quipped.

I found myself lost for words, but eventually said rather weakly, I'd been with a girl or two I'd met in Friedrich Straße bars.

'Probably enemy agents!' he concluded. Throughout the interrogation a Soviet 'friend' sat in a corner, saying nothing. He roared with laughter at some of Mielke's crude formulations and my embarrassment. Mielke then got on to my early background. I pleaded guilty to being a victim of my father's political weakness and my schooling in the Third Reich. 'You've got no documents,' he said accusingly and shaking his finger at me threateningly. How could I have? Königsberg and my official place of birth Allenstein had ceased to exist as German towns and, heavily devastated, were now de facto in the Soviet Union and Poland respectively. He knew this too and was furious about his impotence in this regard. Finally, he said to me, 'I am a loyal son of the Berlin workers and their party. I hate Fascists, opportunists, fairies and people like you. I will destroy you all like vermin. You can watch out you fucker!'

To my utter surprise, I was allowed to leave that forbidding building with its long sinister corridors and after spending a few days in a Berlin police billet I received my orders to report to Colonel Fischer. Much later, I was to learn that Kurt had been arrested as part of Stalin's purge of so-called 'cosmopolitans', mostly Jews. He was released in 1954, a year or so after the dictator's death.

15.

Sergeant Helga and her 'little treasure'

I found Fischer in his new office in the *Hauptabteilung Grenzpolizei und Bereitschaften* (Main Department Frontier Police and Mobile Units). The walls were decorated in the usual way with portraits of Stalin, Lenin and the German Communist leader, Wilhelm Pieck. He gave me an enthusiastic 'Welcome', as though we were old buddies. Presently, his secretary, a uniformed female member of the 'police', brought us coffee and biscuits. He outlined the current situation and our mission. It was likely there would be German armed forces established in the Soviet Zone. We were part of the staff team responsible for making the necessary arrangements on the ground. My job was to deal with any practical problems that landed on my desk and generally assist Fischer. I would also be expected to lecture on ideological matters and prepare training material for the troops.

'Any questions?' he enquired.

'Yes, Colonel, why me?'

'Well you got good reports from Moscow. Secondly, your youth and closeness to our recruits, both in age and military experience, give you an advantage over most of your superiors. We have here Communists who have had either no military experience or only a limited amount in the Spanish War. The others are ex-Wehrmacht and all of us are getting a bit long in the tooth, relatively speaking, to be mixing in with 18 to 25 year olds.'

Put that way it made some sort of sense. 'You keep your rank of lieutenant for the time being. The way things are going you could be Captain Thomas within six months. And by the way, there'll be no more "just pocket money" deals. You'll be getting decent pay,' he added.

After my grilling by Mielke I still felt anxious, but neither of us mentioned it. He concluded, 'Watch your step and you'll go far Thomas. This is a time of great opportunities. But if we falter we could end up in a Soviet labour camp or worse.' It seemed the sword of Damocles was to remain my companion.

I was to meet a number of the 'Moscow Mafia' in the months to come. The Soviets sent back hundreds of officers to join the new units. Heinz Thiel, whom I had met at a conference in Moscow, worked with me on media relations. He had served with the *Großdeutschland* Division as a war correspondent and had been in the Nazi party. He soon abandoned the People's Police for a career with DEFA, the Soviet Zone film company. It was probably a wise choice because we were not completely trusted by our Communist superiors or by the Soviets who remained in overall control. I followed Fischer's advice to 'watch my step', which was not entirely easy because of the changing political line and the in-fighting and petty rivalries which existed. I made myself useful and, almost by accident produced training material which caught the rising tide of the Ulbricht faction of the SED. The thesis of the 'German Road to Socialism' was abandoned and Ulbricht and his friends, taking their cue from Moscow, put ever more emphasis on following the Soviet example. Fischer rewarded my efforts as promised by proposing my promotion to captain and this was duly approved to take effect with the setting up of the German Democratic Republic (GDR/DDR) on 7 October 1949. I was only 23 and, as one of the youngest holding that rank, the prospects looked bright.

Even months after the event, my 'interview' with Mielke still haunted me. It was obvious that the fact that I was not involved with an approved woman could be held against me. We were encouraged to find female friends of our own kind, preferably with women in the service. The trouble was the men vastly outnumbered the women. Without consciously doing so, I started to revise my standards. Perhaps I had been spoiled by Hilde and Galina and my unfulfilled ambitions towards Alexandra. I thought I should come down to reality and 'join the gang' and satisfy my sexual urges where I could - especially if those available had been cleared by Comrade Mielke and our Soviet friends. Among those available was Helga, a comrade of ample proportions, yet not unshapely, with dyed blond hair. She was appointed Fischer's secretary shortly after I arrived. She had had her eye on me from the moment she joined us. Three years older than me, she had worked as an auxiliary in the Luftwaffe, and after a brief internment and 're-education', she had found employment in the new police force. As she was a secretary and a sergeant, I was nominally her superior officer. I soon realised, however, that Fischer depended on not only her secretarial skills but also her 'know all, see all, say nothing' abilities as well. If you got in with her she could give you reliable information on what was going on throughout the Main Department and often beyond it. In this situation there was no point in pulling rank. Fear, ambition and necessity can be corrupting and in that first year of the DDR I was corrupted a little more.

My promotion had impressed Helga and we talked and joked more and more in the office. She dropped hints about changes in policy or personnel which she had heard of before they became official and this enabled me to adjust accordingly. But Helga was getting restless and frustrated. There had to be some form of suitable payment from my side and it would have to be paid in kind. Accordingly, when Helga dropped a heavy hint that the first ball of the Main Department was coming up and was likely to be a grand affair, I was compelled to request the pleasure of her company. She readily accepted. By the standards of the time it was a grand affair with ample supplies of German *Sekt* and Soviet Champagne as well as alcohol to suit more robust proletarian tastes. The food was also excellent and we looked reasonably smart in our new dress uniforms. One guest who put a slight damper on the evening was Comrade Mielke who gave me a long, hard, knowing look which seemed to say, 'You're learning, my boy!' He, of course, realised as well as I that Helga's ambitions would not be fulfilled by a social evening together. When she invited me to go to her flat not far from the compound I was in no position to refuse. It was the beginning of a period of busy nights as well as busy days. Her sexual appetite appeared unrestricted and we had sessions that went long in to the night. I soon ceased to be her superior officer, Hauptmann Thomas, and became her playmate '*Hauptmann Schatzchen*' (Captain Little Treasure).

16.

World Youth Festival, Berlin 1951

For the Third World Games of Youth and Students for Peace from 5 to 19 August, 1951, there was to be a complete security alert. The Festival was a giant affair. On offer were sports competitions, music, both classical and popular, art exhibitions, film shows, dance shows, discussion seminars, and - inevitably - demonstrations and rallies. Officially, the Free German Youth (FDJ) led by Erich Honecker were the official hosts. In reality, the FDJ was controlled by the Party (SED), which in turn was dependent on the Soviet party leadership. It would be relatively easy to control the ideological side of the Festival, but there were many other practical problems. It was impossible to avoid some "free mixing" with delegates from the Socialist Camp and Western young people, some of whom would not be Communists. This could lead to all kinds of complications. Enemy agents could attempt to recruit students from the socialist states during the Festival. Western organisations, above all the Social Democratic

Party, would undoubtedly launch a propaganda blitz on the Festival. There would be attempts to foul up the organisation to create chaos, and therefore, dissatisfaction among the participants. There would also be extra possibilities for normal, non¬-political criminal activities, attempts to steal goods in short supply, the usual pilfering, fraud, theft of participants' property, pick-pocketing and prostitution. It could become a black marketeers' paradise!

This was to be the Republic's first chance to put itself on the map internationally, at a time when it was being boycotted by the West. It was successful in that there were delegations from virtually every Western country, as well as all the Socialist Camp states. Delegations came from a number of Middle East countries such as Lebanon, Syria and Iran, which was, once again, facing British military threats for daring to nationalise its own oil industry. The problems of dealing with such a large and diverse group of people were solved with typical German efficiency and I never heard any major complaints. It must also be remembered that this was achieved in part of a heavily devastated city.

I was detailed to keep an eye on a school in Mahlsdorf on Erich Baronweg 8/9, where a large British contingent was being quartered. I had two members of the People's Police under me; one posing as the caretaker and the other as his assistant. The 'caretaker' had served in the paratroops during the war, and had spent several years as a prisoner of war in the north of England. His English was quite good.

The other had served in a panzer unit before being captured by Monty in North Africa. He too had got to know Britain as a prisoner. Both were members of the SED. Our job was to ensure that our guests did not get into 'trouble'. We also had to keep away hostile elements from them, and thwart possible West German propaganda raids with pamphlets, leaflets and so on. We were also talent spotting. If we found anyone who could be possibly engaged as an agent we were to make overtures. If we found anyone we believed to be a British intelligence agent we were to restrict their activities as much as possible until the delegation left for home. Any arrest, for whatever reason, and however justified, would be more trouble than it was worth.

Specially picked members of the FDJ, who had taken crash courses in English, were put in charge of our British guests. They performed well. The British were warm and friendly, especially so when one remembers it was only six years after the end of the war. Obviously, it was interesting for me to move among young people, some younger and others older than me, who were really my own compatriots. The ones I met appeared to be a good-hearted and intelligent bunch, but many of them were quite naive about our situation, about Germany and about the war. For me it was moving to meet Jewish guests for the first time. The only other Jews I had known were Kurt and Galina. I still remember the enthusiastic and handsome young Communist, Ralph Samuels. There were others from London, Leeds and Manchester. Of course, most of those from Britain were not Jewish. There were the fair-haired, slender girls from southern England, the darker Welsh girls, and one or two red heads. The men were a mixed bunch too. We did not find any enemy agents, though one, a school teacher who spoke fluent German, had been a sergeant in the Royal Army Intelligence Corps in the war. Some had, for us, strange ideas about Socialism. On the whole there was a strong tendency to pacifism which was rejected by the SED. Some were a bit disturbed by the many uniforms they saw, which in the case of the People's Police and the FDJ, were very reminiscent of the Nazi era.

The weather was on the side of 'the Great Stalin,' who sponsored the Festival, which helped to make the outdoor meetings successful. At one of these events on the Alexanderplatz, I got the surprise of my life. I saw someone I thought I knew in the crowd. My heart pounded faster. It really was her. She looked marvellous. How would she react to me? I felt foolish. Despite all that I had seen and done, despite my amorous liaisons, I was back again to how I was with Dorothy a decade before. I waited until she looked in my direction. Our eyes met. 'Martin Thomas, is it you?' I went up to her and somewhat awkwardly planted kisses on both her cheeks. We talked excitedly about anything that came into our heads. Alexandra was there as a group leader with the Soviet Communist Youth, the *Konsomol*. She would be in Berlin another week. Thank God for that, I thought. She was not married. I explained, as best I could, my situation. Despite our official commitments we managed to meet five or six times over the following days. We talked and talked. I wanted to have her, difficult though it was to be alone, but she refused. She let me touch her but I got little response.

'You have another,' she said. I tried to make it clear to her that it was her I loved and it probably always would be her. She explained that she believed me and thought 'probably' was a silly word to use.

'You know you will always love me and I am bound to you in the same way for ever. We really knew that when we met in Moscow. But it was not to be that we should be together. You and I know that you cannot just love anybody. There are few people you really love. We are chained together emotionally. We cannot get away from that. I knew I would see you in Berlin. That was the whole point of the visit, even though I did not know your address and did not know what you were doing.'

As we sat by the River Havel, she told me, 'You will satisfy yourself, with your German Frau Helga, that's all right, but you will go on loving me. I will marry some Andrei or Vladimir, but I will go on loving you. We will do our duty. Sadly, that is our fate.

We watched the closing ceremonies hand in hand. A band played and a massed choir sang the Festival song, 'Friendship will be victorious.' There was a massive fireworks display which included a giant portrait of our benefactor, teacher, protector and friend, Comrade Stalin. Alexandra flew back to Moscow the next day. Two weeks later I received a letter from her, part of which I remember by heart, 'You will always be with me in every stage of my life. I will draw strength from you. I am yours forever' I felt I would go crazy. I was filled with joy knowing that she felt this way, but I was ripped apart knowing we were unlikely ever to be together. I told myself this friendship, this 'love', was nonsense. It ran counter to all my Marxist beliefs, it was 'illogical' and yet, try as I would to explain it away, to rid myself of it, it stayed with me. She stayed with me. The thought of her influenced my decision-making on several important occasions. My attitude to people changed. For one thing, I became far more tolerant, kinder and more generous. A part of me which was hidden away in the recesses of my body and mind was permanently sad, yet at the same time I was known as a cheerful, reliable and stable personality.

17.

Helga's Peccadilloes

Uniforms had been an important part of Helga's life. The eldest child of an East Berlin tailor, she had learned how to handle men by helping to bring up her three brothers after their mother died of TB. Born in 1923, she was truly part of the Nazi generation. Wearing her dad's SA cap, she formed her own storm squad consisting of her brothers and two of their friends. Her father had been an apprentice uniform maker before the 1914-18 war, but there had been little call for uniforms after it. With his wife, a dress maker, he had been forced to go into general tailoring. He resented having to fight for work against the rising retail chains selling ready-made clothes, and against Jewish competitors in the neighbourhood around Oranienburger Straße, who seemed to be prepared to work for nothing. Hitler changed all that after 1933 and he rejoiced in being able to return to his original specialism, uniforms. Helga had watched the customers, the arrogant overbearing ones, those whose shyness did not match their splendid

uniforms, the unsure ones who sought to prove themselve
by arguing over every button and every mark. She admire
the heroic officer-types and despised the civilians wh
thought they could become important just by donning SA
uniforms. Her dad was more of the second type, but he wa
an exception. She liked best of all, the new air forc
uniform and the men who wore it. When she was olde
around fifteen in 1938, she had secretly tried on one or tw
and stood admiring herself in the long mirrors of the fittin;
room. She would have loved to be one of the great wome
aviators of the 1930s like Hanna Reitsch, who went on t
become the only woman to receive the Iron Cross, firs
class.

After successfully completing her grammar school leavin,
exam at sixteen, Helga had worked as a secretary. She sti
lived at home and met many of her father's customers
helping in the shop on occasions. When a handsome youn
air force officer asked her out she demurely accepted. O
their third cinema date they saw Werner Hochbaum'
heavy breathing melodrama, *They're Talking Abo*
Jacqueline, about a foolish femme fatale. It made Helg
feel guilty because of her flirtatious ways. When he
officer proposed she accepted. Within weeks they wer
being married in Berlin's 'red town hall'. But the
happiness, if that's what it was, did not last long. He die
when his Dornier 17, a light bomber, spun out of contro
whilst on a sortie, somewhere over southern England o
one sunny day in September 1940. Helga was just one c
thousands of war brides who became war widows. She wa

glad they had not given the Fatherland a new son or daughter. Once it became possible for women to volunteer as auxiliaries she had rushed to join the Luftwaffe. She had enjoyed the life, the excitement and, in the last phase, being part of an anti-aircraft gun crew. Surrender to the Soviets had been a pretty grim experience. However, one of her captors, a captain in the engineers, who spoke some German, had got her into his office and inevitably into his bed. In both locations she had worked hard at mastering Russian. She had succeeded. By the time he was posted back to Moscow, she had convinced the new rulers that she was reliable and she had no difficulty in entering the police service.

Most of Helga's own 'storm squad' died either on the Eastern front or in Italy. The older of her two brothers was lucky; he was captured by the British in North Africa. Her father survived the bombing of Berlin, and its 'liberation', and earned a few crusts of bread making uniforms for Soviet officers. Helga's captain of engineers was the first and recommended her father to his successors. The old man died nearly blind in 1948.

Having had to do most of the cooking as a girl, Helga had become proficient in terms of knowing how to make a little go a long way, how to dress up common mundane dishes, and how to provide something a little special. All these skills were exercised on me. I was putting on weight rapidly. Helga also saw to it that I was immaculately turned out. She inspected my uniform several times a week. After each new culinary delight, each overnight stay, each bit of gossip confided, I found my resolve to extricate myself from Helga weaken further. It was, dare I say it, comfortable. I knew she saw me as a husband - and sooner rather than later. The other factor was that I had heard nothing more from Hilde or Galina and just got the occasional card from Alexandra. The months of silence had turned into years. My life with Helga and my professional life were becoming settled. I estimated that if I stayed on I could make major easily and, in time, probably colonel. That presumed my true identity was not revealed. If I were to be exposed I would either be charged with making false statements when I joined the People's Police or be accused of being a spy. In either case my career in the German People's Police in Barracks would be over. The Cold War, which had started almost after the end of hostilities in 1945, had got worse year by year. The three Western powers, the USA, Britain and France were on a collision course with the Soviet Union. West Germany was firmly in the Western camp and we were firmly in the Soviet camp. In 1952, the para-military People's Police in Barracks was set up with officers like General Vincenz Müller, who had served in two World Wars and appeared to have no political allegiances, at their head. They were recognised as armed forces in practice if not in name armed as they were with artillery, armoured vehicles and T-34 tanks. We were to be part of the new force. Fischer clapped his hands and smacked his lips whilst contemplating new promotion for himself and his staff.

With the change of status, our lives were further circumscribed. We were not supposed to have contact with friends or family members in any Western country including West Berlin. We were not supposed to visit any Western country including West Berlin. I felt very guilty about not at least attempting to contact my mother but what could I do? As Berlin was not yet divided by the notorious Wall, it was difficult to keep all our members from visiting the Western sectors of the city. Often the dividing line ran along quite narrow streets, even through buildings in the most extreme cases. There was everything to buy in West Berlin. In our 'Democratic Sector', on the other hand, there were constant shortages. It was so tempting just to cross the street to buy bananas, oranges or other fruit or vegetables from a humble West Berlin corner green grocer's shop. Even though such purchases were expensive for us, paid as we were in East marks, which could only be exchanged at something like four East marks for one West mark, the temptation was strong. Helga, with her sense of adventure, curiosity and a wish to please me, could not resist the temptation. I warned her, even begged her, not to do it. Having got used to going - in what was after all her own home city - she got more daring and went farther afield to the streets around Kurfürstendamm to buy other items such as clothing. For my 26th birthday she gave me a special treat. There was a particularly good steak dish with mushroom sauce helped along with a good Beaujolais wine. She had decorated the room with candles. My present was an expensive light blue shirt and a silk tie. After the meal she left me alone for a few minutes and went into the bedroom. Then, she called me in. She was dressed in elegant black lingerie with black stockings and suspenders to match. She looked very seductive in these products which were impossible to get in our sector. After my long nights with Hilde, who was no stranger to this get-up, I always had a penchant for this, particularly the flesh in between the top of the stockings and suspender belt. After considerable fun and games we put out the candles and dozed off. It seemed like only seconds later though when we were startled by loud banging on the door. I thought they were using sledge hammers. As it was her flat she opened the door. In sprang five men in civilian clothes from the Ministry of State Security. 'Enjoying yourselves, comrades?' sneered the leader. They ordered us to dress and, after searching the flat, they called on us to follow them to two awaiting cars advising us to give no trouble. Stunned and still a little dazed, we meekly followed their instructions.

18.

1953: A surprising offer in the lion's den

After only a quick glance at each other we were driven off at great speed in separate cars. There were not many people about in the grey dawn of this humbled city. Within perhaps fifteen minutes we had reached our destination. A red and white painted barrier was raised to let the vehicles through. I was told to get out and ordered to follow into the old dark building which looked like a converted derelict factory. I was then ordered to stand facing a wall. After a while I was forced to strip totally naked and given a body search. I stood there naked for some time, my teeth chattering every now and then due to the cold. My clothes minus belt, tie and shoe laces were later returned. Eventually, I was locked in a small, windowless, cold, damp cell below ground. Apart from a mattress and two blankets and a metal bucket, the only other furnishing was the graffiti on the walls. A malevolent silence fell over the place. At one point I felt as though I was going short of breath. I had the feeling the guard peeped through the Judas hole at me from time to time. Sleep was difficult; I must have been hallucinating as I did not know when I was dreaming in my sleep and when I was simply day dreaming. I was overcome by this great Angst, and the feeling, 'Why me?' Fear and boredom gripped me, then resignation followed by defiance. During perhaps two days in the semi-darkness of the isolation cell I had thought over my position and my life. I was sick of these stupid little people trying to bully me and was determined to fight back.

'Like the accommodation comrade captain?' my interrogator asked mockingly. 'Enjoy it, it could get very much worse, believe me, if you don't come up with the right answers.'

'I've experienced worse, ...far worse,' I replied defiantly. The thought of what I'd overcome, both physically and mentally, in the war years helped to keep me going during the next few days, weeks and months. Every aspect of my life was, once again, put under the microscope and dissected in the greatest detail. I knew I had just to keep my head because there was no evidence against me. Evidence of what? Evidence of anything!

After several months held without any contact with the outside world, I was suddenly faced with a new member of the Ministry for State Security. He was altogether different in his attitude. I was informed that Helga had confessed everything and it was clear I had had nothing to do with her activities in West Berlin. He regretted that it had taken so long to sort out the matter. But added, that I was guilty of dereliction of duty in that I had not denounced Helga, and I had also benefited by her illegal money changing and purchases. However, in view of my past services they wanted to help me. 'We should be able to sort things out in a more civilised manner in a socialist state,' he conceded apologetically.

During the days that followed I was given the chance to take regular showers, wear clean clothes and eat nourishing food. I'm sure that I'd lost a good couple of kilos during my ordeal. I was also given several issues of *Neues Deutschland* to read. While I had been incarcerated the Great Stalin had died and the enemy had attempted to exploit both this and the economic difficulties of the German Democratic Republic. On 17 June 1953 and in the days that followed, the unthinkable had happened. Sections of the workers had gone on strike. Various elements of the Party had faltered and agents of Nazi General Gehlen from West Germany had attempted to exploit the situation. They had been crushed with the help of the Red Army. Everything was under control and our party, the SED, had learned from its mistakes, including the Ministry of State Security. I was now being asked to help sort out the difficulties and to help the SED to make the New Course a success. It was difficult to take it all in. What did it mean that Stalin was dead? Galina had said that he had been unaware of all the crimes being committed in the vast Socialist Camp. But apparently the 'good guys' had won and I was being asked to help as one of the 'good guys'. This seemed to appear sensible particularly at this juncture. Among the 'bad guys' was the head of the Soviet secret police, Lavrenty Beria, who had attempted to seize control following Stalin's death, but he was arrested, sentenced and then executed. There had been changes too at the top of the Ministry for State Security, the Stasi. The world was changing for the better with the new Soviet leadership. I signed the necessary papers agreeing to work secretly for the Stasi. I was to return to my job in the People's Police in Barracks and keep an eye on things. I would occasionally write secret reports on developments, the mood of the men, any sign of defeatism, deviationism and that dreaded disease, Social Democratism. My colleagues would have to be kept in the dark about my new function. What about Helga? I was to forget about her. She had let me down and let the SED down, as well as, the Workers' and Peasants' State. They had treated her generously, released her but she had simply defected to the class enemy.

The sun was shining brightly as I was, at last, on my way to a new posting in the People's Police in Barracks in August 1953. I was given the rank of major and told I was not to reveal where I had spent the last few months. As far as anyone knew I had been on staff training for my promotion from captain to major. Some of my new colleagues treated me with suspicion believing that I had been for training in the Soviet Union and was, therefore, likely to get early preferment. They also suspected that I was a plant of the Soviet 'friends'. I must admit I was not very happy with the situation but I attempted to make a success of the new assignment. I filed the secret reports required of me whilst getting on with my open, official duties. By the standards of the 1940s and early 1950s life in the People's Police was more relaxed. This was also true of life outside it.

Further changes were taking place. In January 1956, the Republic officially admitted to having armed forces. The setting up of the National People's Army (NVA) under a Ministry for Defence was announced. Our unit was simply incorporated into the NVA. I remained a major and, I must admit, I felt a little let down that I had not received further promotion. In February 1956, the Party faced another challenge. At the 20th Congress of the Communist Party of the Soviet Union, Nikita Khrushchev denounced Stalin as a tyrant who had the blood of millions on his hands. The Soviet leader's speech was not printed in the Socialist Camp, but was leaked to the Western press and was widely reported. We received a summary for internal party consumption only. It was a shock. It appeared Stalin was not much better than Hitler. A few old Communists killed themselves in despair, others left the Party. Some of the younger elements felt a surge of hope. I had twice been a victim of Stalinist methods. The way we were treated as prisoners of war was not compatible with Socialist principles, nor was my more recent treatment at the hands of the Stasi. My mentor, Kurt, in Moscow, had been wrongly accused. Released after Stalin's demise, somehow he managed to find a recent address of mine and I got a short letter from him saying he was well and urging me to 'have hope, remain loyal and keep on the road'.

One other cause for hope were the Soviet Union's space successes. In October 1957, to the surprise of the West, the Soviets put the first artificial earth satellite into space. After that, a whole string of successes, including putting the first man in space - Major Yuri Gagarin - revealed their decisive lead over the Americans. Gagarin toured the world and did much to improve the image of the Soviet Homeland. Soviet doctrine was defined as 'Peaceful Co-existence', East and West were to avoid destructive military clashes and to compete peacefully to see which the superior system was. This sounded entirely sensible in the nuclear age. Were we at last on the right road?

After nearly three years in my NVA job, I was beginning to feel I was in a rut and somewhat lonely. After Helga I was more careful about any involvement with women. I took up running and other sporting activity in the Society for Sport and Technology (GST). Through voluntary work in this para-military sports organisation, I had plenty of opportunity to meet splendid examples of socialist womanhood, but somehow I could not get emotionally involved. There was a fair amount of casual sex which was rampant in our part of Germany. This was not very satisfactory and masturbation even less so. I was lonely. My loneliness was made far worse by what had become a routine, undemanding job. In times of intense activity and success, lack of a companion is not as obvious. In this situation I received a telephone call one afternoon in March of 1956. I was told by the caller, who identified himself as from the Stasi, to keep the call confidential. I was told to report to a safe house in the Berlin suburb of Pankow for a 'conspiratorial meeting' the following week. The house was an old villa which was as shabby as the other buildings on Kavalier Straße. I pressed the bell button marked 'Schmidt' and was ushered in by a well-dressed man of roughly my own age (29) who had obviously undergone military training in some army or other. Everything about the place gave the impression that the previous owners had fled or been thrown out in 1945, and that since then it had been used mercilessly by Soviet and then East German security officials. Little or no attempt had been made to adapt it for its new purpose, to clean it on a daily or regular basis, or to care for it in any way. I was asked to sit down and offered a drink. Opposite me sat Major General Hans Fruck, who looked older than his 45 years. As I was later to learn, he had just been appointed Deputy Head of the *Hauptverwaltung Aufklärung* (Main Administration Reconnaissance or HVA) of the Ministry for State Security. The job of the HVA was simply espionage beyond the borders of the German Democratic Republic. After being imprisoned for his anti-Nazi resistance activities, this Berlin engineering turner, Fruck, had risen rapidly through the ranks of the People's Police after 1945. He had been in the Stasi since its foundation in 1950. He obviously knew a great deal about me and after verifying several points about my past offered me a job in his department. He claimed that despite the apparent relative peace between East and West this was a time of great danger. The mistakes and even crimes of Stalin, Beria and others had created ideological confusion and uncertainty in the Socialist Camp. The Imperialists could strike at any time, tempted as they were to exploit this situation. There was a desperate need to infiltrate every aspect of West German life and various NATO institutions. I was being asked to work actively for peace on the 'silent front'. It was a psychologically tough but interesting, even exciting, life. My dossier showed that I had the necessary qualities. Comrade General Minister Mielke thought so. 'I believe you have had several encounters with him,' Fruck said with a thin smile. It was a very tempting offer and thus I accepted the challenge and another new chapter in my life.

19.

Disappointment and sorrow in 1961

My work for the Ministry for State Security was concerned largely with Britain. My job was reading and analysing the British press, published government documents, listening to the BBC, and writing weekly reports on the developing situation. Occasionally reports came in from 'a reliable source in the operative area', from 'George' or from some other agent. Twice a year I was treated to the luxury of staying at a good hotel in Leipzig where British businessmen, tourists and politicians, like the Labour MPs Ian Mikardo or Will Owen, were staying for the trade fair. I kept my eye open for any possible contacts or indiscretions and was also required to eavesdrop on their conversations. Sometimes I visited West Berlin to go unobtrusively to British cultural events or to take a drink in bars frequented by British servicemen. I was regarded as too valuable to 'blow my cover' by a failed recruitment gamble. Others, however, were required to do that once I had succeeded in targeting an individual. This was a rarity.

Thus, my years at the Stasi were going by. I remained a bachelor despite one or two encounters with female colleagues which did not last.

One bright summer morning in 1958 I got a call in my office from the Soviet Embassy. I must say I was very surprised. Despite the supposedly close relationship with our Soviet allies, in practice, we had little to do with them. The diplomat at the other end of the line said, 'One moment Comrade, I've got someone who wants to speak with you.' I was stunned, breathless, almost in tears when I heard her voice. It was Alexandra. She had wangled a trip to East Berlin on some semi-journalistic assignment covering the V Congress of the SED. Her contact in the embassy had used his influence to get my number. She had a room in one of the few old, good hotels on Friedrichstraße and it was there that we met. We had not met since 1955 when she had been briefly in Berlin to give a lecture on '"The Thaw" and Soviet Literature', and had little contact except for one or two cards and letters each year since then. Yet, within minutes the old magic was working again. She was now 35 but to me she looked lovelier than ever. We both had our official obligations to our respective employers and masters, yet we managed to see each other six times over the next week. We went to the state opera on the Unter den Linden and I could not help feeling very proud at the interval when so many admiring, curious eyes turned in our direction. Our only rivals were a group of British RAF officers in full-dress uniforms and their ladies 'showing the flag' and taking advantage of the, for them, cheap tickets. We walked around the beautiful Müggelsee and on another occasion broke the rules and slipped into West Berlin for a day's shopping combined with a boat trip on Lake Wannsee. We sat together in the royal gardens of the Cecilienhof in Potsdam. We talked endlessly over long suppers in the Ganymed restaurant near the Brecht theatre and in the Budapest restaurant on Frankfurter Allee. Somehow we never consummated our love, not that I would have been unwilling but there was respect. She had married in the meantime and greatly admired her husband, a well-known public figure, who had fought against Stalinism. I did not want to jeopardise her marriage in any way and felt I had little to offer a Russian so tied to Moscow. I was, in effect, a prisoner of my personal history and present circumstances. Sometimes I thought we had been stupid and idealistic and that we should have seized the moment. If it was anyone's fault it was mine. Sometimes her eyes told me she would have taken little persuasion. The way she took my arm, held my hand or hugged me told me. Her eyes, as we kissed good night, told me. Despite this lack of physical fulfilment we knew we loved each other and that we would always be tied together by an invisible, yet unbreakable bond, 'till death do us part', and, who knows, perhaps beyond. We said our 'Au Revoir' on the crowded Alexanderplatz station as she left for Schönefeld air field. I know she cried after the S-Bahn left the station, so did I.

Walter Ulbricht, our leader, made many promises at the SED congress. The most dramatic of these was the aim to overtake West Germany in the consumption of most consumer goods and foods in the new five-year plan period. He talked about, 'Overtaking the Federal Republic without catching it up.' This ridiculous formulation became the propaganda catch phrase. Some thought because they could not understand it, it showed the brilliance of Ulbricht. It was surprising how many comrades believed him. We in the Ministry, like our colleagues in the other ministries, the Party apparatus and the armed forces, were cut off to a degree from everyday reality. Unlike many ordinary East Berliners most of us did not normally visit West Berlin and certainly not West Germany. We tended to have our social contacts within the SED, and we often inter-married. We had better housing than the average citizen, better chances of getting tickets to important theatrical or similar events and to top sports meetings. We had the option of shopping in special, better stocked shops located within the buildings where we worked. We were encouraged to take our holidays at the increasing number of Ministry holiday camps, rest homes and hotels. Usually, our reading was the Party paper *Neues Deutschland* and we were not expected to listen to Western radio stations or watch Western television which developed in the 1960s. Fortuitously, because of my work I was expected to follow the Western media including those of Britain. Unlike some of my colleagues therefore, I was more sceptical, but I freely admit, I did think that although the promises would not be met, there would be a great surge forwards. The opposite was to happen.

Our economic situation in 1958-9 was not bad; things had improved. The people were less restive. This was shown by the reduction in those 'voting with their feet' and going West over the open 'frontier' in Berlin. In 1959, 'only' 143,917 people turned their backs on the workers' and peasants' state. This was the best year, from this point of view, in the Republic's history. Instead of consolidating on the basis of the existing arrangements, Ulbricht decided it was time to build 'comprehensive Socialism', which included the nationalisation of the remaining private middle-sized businesses, the collectivisation of the land, and more 'class struggle'. Thus, in 1960, 198,188 left, and in the first half of 1961 the figures climbed higher. In the summer rumours abounded. Ulbricht would be removed, the GDR was collapsing, another 7 June (workers' revolt) was coming and East Berlin would be sealed off from the West to stop the haemorrhaging. Sadly, it was the rumour about a possible sealing-off which proved correct. We were faced with a full security alert and leave was cancelled for all personnel. We even slept in the office. We were warned to be ready for possible action. Dismayed by The Wall, we were totally surprised at the lack of Western action against it. President Kennedy did nothing, nor did the West German leader, the 'Old Fox' Adenauer. West Berlin Mayor, Willy Brandt, said harsh words but was impotent. We spent our time studying the Western media for reactions and the reports of our agents on NATO military movements. A mood of depression swept over our ranks. At Party meetings we were told to be optimistic. At last we were on the road to complete success. There would be no more economic failures due to lack of manpower and uncertainty. People now knew there was no way out and they would have to make the best of things. We should have taken such steps years before. Now the Republic would go forward. Gradually, we accepted the change.

The year 1961 had another blow in store for me personally. I was devastated to get a letter from Nicole, Alexandra's husband, to say she had died, aged 38, giving birth to twins. One of the twins she had been carrying had died too. He was now left to bring up their older daughter Yelena, and his baby, whom he intended to call Martin. She had spoken of me many times especially in her last days. He knew she had always loved me. He wished me well. I took out the few letters and cards I had, perhaps on average three a year plus New Year's greeting cards. There were also two or three photographs. I wept and wept, and sought comfort in her restrained words of love, admiration and esteem. I knew she would always be a part of me. I threw myself even deeper into my work which became therapy but also an escape from real life.

20.

A new identity, a new adventure

Every ministry and every department of every ministry had its targets in each five-year plan period; ours was no exception. The HVA was ordered to expand its activities. Our principal activities were, and remained, directed against West Germany, but it was thought we had not exploited our opportunities elsewhere as much as we should have done. Posing as West Germans, we could infiltrate other NATO and neutral states without too much difficulty. Thousands of our agents had been sent over with the refugees before August 1961. This would now become slightly more complicated because the flood of refugees had been reduced to a trickle. Nevertheless, various possibilities existed. We could pose as ethnic Germans who had been allowed to leave the Soviet Union or, more likely, Poland. We could take on the identity of a West German who lived permanently abroad. If we were to work outside West Germany we could take on the identity of a West German still living there. To my surprise, I was offered such a 'holiday' abroad. My command of English and knowledge of the country, through my diligent reading of the British press and the latest literature, like John Braine's *Room At The Top*, and not least, my reliability, were thought to make me an ideal candidate. Worries about the fact that I had no relatives in the Republic to make me want to come home were put aside. It was felt I could be more resourceful as a loner.

I was sent for training to a school in the country, which had previously belonged to a Nazi organisation and was now disguised as a school of the Society for Sports and Technology. There, our small group, even with a new temporary identity, studied British history, manners and customs, geography, the political and economic system and, of course, the language. Most of it was a waste of time from my point of view. In addition there was no one among the instructors who had any recent first-hand knowledge of Britain. They were anti-Nazi émigrés who had spent all, or part, of the Hitler years there. There was one former Nazi diplomat who had been there in the 1930s. The only English person we met was John Peet, a former Chief Reuters correspondent in West Berlin, who had 'defected' to the German Democratic Republic in June 1950. He gave a series of amusing guest lectures. We were also taught the arts and crafts of espionage: how to think on your feet; how to avoid being followed; the use of invisible ink, codes, dead letter boxes, and small arms; elementary psychology when attempting to recruit subagents. Once again, in my case, most of this knowledge was never to be put to the test.

After successfully completing the course, without, for some strange reason, gaining first class in English language, I was ordered to a conspiratorial meeting with Hans Fruck in the Berlin suburb of Hohenschönhausen. I later discovered that between 1951 and 1989 East Germany's Stasi secret police had used this site (originally set up by the Soviet NKVD) as a detention centre cum prison for un-sentenced suspects. Holding mainly political prisoners it was infamous for the regime of physical and psychological torture meted out to inmates. With the fall of the Communism and the disbanding of the Stasi, the prison was converted into a memorial museum, the *Gedenkstätte Berlin-Hohenschönhausen*, on the initiative of former prisoners.

My mission was simple enough. Posing as a journalist, I was to penetrate the British political establishment. Secondly, I was to attempt to recruit 'by any means' female secretaries who either were already, or were likely to be, working in NATO or other sensitive offices. I was to act as a pathfinder. If my mission proved successful others would follow. I was given the identity of a real West German citizen who had emigrated to the United States in 1955. He was my age, nearly 36, had lived in West Berlin where he had arrived in 1945 from East Prussia. I was supposed to write for a number of publications. One of them was the well-known weekly *Der Spiegel*, which

Fruck assured me had been infiltrated. He gave me the name of one of the editorial staff who would vouch for me if asked. He also gave me the names of two journalists on regional West German papers who were awaiting the occasional contribution from me, which would be published. Everything appeared to have been thought of. In the age of nuclear stalemate, Fruck went on, 'the fight for peace was more vital than ever, and the class struggle had to be carried on by other means.'

Fruck gave me identity documents, several thousand pounds in cash, and the number of a Swiss Banking Corporation account in Zurich. I was to open an account in a London bank into which money would be paid on a monthly basis from Switzerland. I would be taken across the Czech frontier by courier to Austria. From there I would go quite normally to Switzerland picking up Swiss stamps in my passport. I was required to buy new clothes in Austria and Switzerland before flying on to London from Zurich. I had an address in West Germany, actually Hamburg, to which I could send my coded messages through the post. I thanked the General for the confidence he was showing in me and he wished me a 'Gute Reise', 'Bon Voyage'. I was full of excitement and quiet confidence.

It was difficult to prepare for my journey because I was getting a new identity. I was leaving Martin Thomas behind and becoming Martin Braun. This meant I had to hand over all my documents, all my clothes, pictures and so on, once we crossed the Czech frontier. I simply put on my oldest clothes and made sure I had no personal photographs on me. I had lots of time before the train from Berlin-Lichtenberg left for Dresden, the jumping off point of my adventure, so I sat and had a long drink. I consumed three quarters of a bottle of Bulgarian red wine and listened to a record. I did not choose Prokofiev, Shostakovich, de Falla, the songs of Hanns Eisler or the German or Russian classics; I chose Richard Strauss's Don Juan. 'Out and away to new conquests as long as the ardent pulse of youth is beating.' Had I come together with Alexandra, I know I would never have taken on the assignment. Strauss had long fascinated me both because of his music and because of his courage and compromises in the Third Reich. I looked round my 'Socialist' flat built just before the ornate Stalinesque buildings of the 1950s. It comprised two rooms, kitchen and bathroom providing not much space for even my modest requirements. My personal belongings did not add up to much: an oriental rug, which Galina had given me, a model of *Fachwerkhaus*, which was in fact a table lamp from Helga, two Meissen china vases, one slightly damaged through my clumsiness, also from Helga, a Russian landscape painting and a Rosenthal ashtray both from Alexandra, a silly cuckoo clock from Thuringia, the product of a crazy weekend with a woman colleague, a bust of Marx given to me by NVA colleagues as a good-natured joke because they regarded me as a Marx-swot, and one or two shields for sporting achievements from the People's Police. There were also my records, my books, a TV set I never seemed to use, and the furniture, little of which would fetch much on the open market. Before I got too melancholy, I put on my coat, stepped out and I locked the door not knowing when I would return. The key went into the mail box at the entrance of the block of flats.

On the train I had a first class compartment to myself, while the alcohol helped me to sleep for an hour or so. Muddled waves of my past swept through my head, I was on the retreat to Berlin again. Alexandra and my mother were begging me to take them with me but the train we were in would not stop and I could not reach out to them to pull them on to it. We passed Kurt in concentration camp uniform, shot through the head by the side of the track. Then I was being exposed as a fraud by von Frankenberg, and Mielke was smiling a sickly smile close to my face. I awoke in a sweat to the cry '*Alle Aussteigen, Bitte*' (All get off please.) We had reached the dimly-lit station of Dresden. At the end of the platform a man of about my own age, in a long leather jacket, stepped forward and said, 'Are you the man for the Dynamo team?' I replied in the affirmative and he took me to a waiting Wartburg car. Within a short time we had crossed the Czech frontier and he wished me a good and safe journey, not realising that his passenger had just changed identity.

21.

1962: Lots of surprises in the homeland I never knew

My Swiss-Air flight from Zurich was very comfortable and I was particularly impressed with the in-flight catering - far better than most East Germans could ever dream of. Heathrow, London's main airport, came as a bit of a surprise after the only other Western airport I knew, Cologne/Bonn. By comparison, the latter was like a village airstrip, while at Heathrow there were so many planes from such a wide variety of airlines - and so many passengers. But I was also surprised that you had to take a bus or taxi to the underground station at Hounslow to get into central London. On the underground a man lay sprawled on the seats taking up space for at least five people. No one attempted to rouse him. Was he drunk or was he ill? No one seemed to want to get involved. After about an hour or so, I changed at Leicester Square and he travelled on into oblivion. Another big change for me was getting used to so many people from other continents, particularly West

Indians and Asians from Pakistan, India and Malaysia. Later I came across Australians, Cypriots, Italians, Jews, Poles, South Africans and Ukrainians. I had never experienced such a cosmopolitan city before. The general untidiness of the streets and the underground was another surprise. In my mind's eye the British were tall, clean and athletic. Months later I had a different kind of surprise. Like so many Germans I believed that London, at least in winter, was permanently shrouded in fog. This image was the result of so many Sherlock Holmes films with Basil Rathbone as the intellectual super-sleuth.

At Leicester Square I changed to the Northern Line and eventually emerged at Highgate. I had got temporary B&B lodging not far from the station through an accommodation agency. On my arrival at the Victorian house I was surprised yet again. My landlady, Mrs Hurley, turned out to be a wiry, blonde German of 40 something. She was one of a wave of Germans recruited after the war to work in British hospitals. Having found herself a suitable husband, she had stayed on. I could see from the lascivious way she looked at me that she was estimating my potential with an experienced eye. Divorced, she had six lodgers, including myself, all of them men under 40. There was an Indian trainee accountant, an LSE (London School of Economics) student from 'somewhere up north', a divorced sales rep, an Italian learning English and, strangely, a German student there to improve his English. From the noise from his room he spent more time on the Beatles than on his English. Mrs Hurley regarded herself as a connoisseur of the English language and as its guardian. 'You speak beautiful English, you know. Not many Germans reach your level of mastery.' It was a relief to know I had her approval. She preferred not to have blacks in the house, 'No thanks Mr Braun, they frighten me. I don't want some big, burly, black, brute ravishing me.' She quizzed me as she showed me my room. It was furnished with an assortment of conflicting styles which all had one thing in common; they had been new many years before. The only heating was a small gas fire which was, no doubt, totally inadequate in winter. As mine was a 'superior' room it contained a small wash basin with a mirror above it. She assured me I would be very comfortable and relieved me of the first week's rent in advance. As I counted out the new crisp notes she cried with delight, 'Brillo.' I soon learned this was one of her favourite catchphrases.

On my second night in London I thought I ought to savour some of the famous London pub life. It turned out to be a night of shocks and excitement. I took the Northern line southbound from Highgate. At Archway, a young woman wearing the new fashion, a mini-skirt, got in and sat opposite me. I was quite taken aback by such an undue expanse of leg and thigh. I thought to myself, 'I'm going to enjoy living here.' Perhaps my eyes belied my interest - the woman flirted before disembarking. I had seen nothing like it in East Berlin, Vienna or Switzerland for that matter. Getting out of the underground at Leicester Square, I started wandering around Piccadilly with its flashing neon lights. Seeing a sign, White Hart Inn, I entered. I was soon on my way out again. I was shocked to find that I had walked right into a bar frequented by homosexuals. I then turned north and worked my way through the narrow streets of Soho passing a number of young women offering services of one kind or another. Passing a police patrol, it was hard to believe British police still appeared to be unarmed. On Dean St I stumbled upon the Italian restaurant Quo Vadis? The food was not bad, the cost not too high, the service was the surprise. Even in Bonn or Hamburg or West Berlin I had never been in a restaurant with so many waiters and so few guests. It was obviously a well-known place judging from the photographs of famous people who had eaten there, which lined the walls. One famous person not recorded was Karl Marx. He and his family had lived in the upper part of the building in dire poverty in the 1840s. Presumably it was not then a restaurant. Walking the streets I soon realised that Soho was a quarter which had a secret as well as an open life. In the windows of paper shops there were so many offers of French lessons such as 'French lessons available by native speaker, strict discipline enforced.' There were also hundreds of 'models' on offer. After several hours of wandering, and a last drink, in the Nellie Dean pub, I made my way to Tottenham Court Rd underground and caught the tube direct to Highgate.

It was probably 11p.m. when I arrived back only to find my Yale key would not move the lock. I was forced to knock and then bang. Presently, a light was switched on in the hall and my landlady appeared at the door. 'Oh, Mr

Braun,' she said in English with her strong German accent, 'I thought you were already in. Forgive me. I wouldn't lock you out for the world. I insist you come and have a drink with me as recompense for the inconvenience I have caused you.' It would have served little purpose to say no, so I didn't. She led me into her dimly-lit room where dusty Chinese vases abounded and thick orient rugs covered the floor. We sat together on a large, worn, leather sofa in front of which a nearly full bottle of Liebfraumilch awaited our pleasure. It was not long before her floral, silk, kimono, was falling from her shoulders revealing her neat skinny body and ample bosom. She said she had been very lonely since her husband left for Australia. I was very understanding and set about my task.

Mrs Hurley was the type of woman I'd heard about but never encountered and would become obsessive; that soon became clear to me. After only a week of her favours we parted company. In any case I needed a flat on my own without any restrictions and any unwanted interest. I found a 'luxury' flat in a converted Victorian house near Hampstead Heath. It had a large bed-sitting room furnished in Scandinavian style with a kitchen and bathroom. My landlord was a Jewish immigrant from Central Europe who was rapidly expanding his empire across north London. My neighbours were a young, newly-wed, Dutch couple above me, and a screaming, alcoholic, Swedish academic couple above them. We had little to do with each other. The flat was convenient for the railway station and the 73 bus which went directly into the West End of central

London. Occasionally, I walked on the Heath and saw a face I thought I had seen on television. One face I did know was that of Michael Foot, MP, the Labour politician, who walked his dog there regularly. I thought of approaching him, but in the end did not.

believe in it either. 'Alternatively...alternatively, you could come to my summer garden party. It's a very modest and informal affair.'

I thought that would be more up my street. So, the following Saturday I made my way by overland train from Victoria to Shortlands station in Bromley, Kent. David lived on Kingswood Road, a short walk from the station, in a small, three-bedroom detached early post-war house with gardens back and front. Like myself, still a bachelor, I found him playing host to about 30 guests in the back garden. He greeted me effusively, 'So glad to see you, Michael... sorry, SORRY, Martin, come and have a drink. What can I do you for? Will red wine do?'

'Fine,' I responded. Sausages were sizzling on a barbecue. Salad, cubes of cheese, baked potatoes and freshly cut bread were set out on a table alongside glasses of red and white wine. There were also bowls of crisps and nuts on offer.

'You can have some of these lovely sausages in a minute...Make that five,' said a rather sweaty, slightly younger, man tending the sausages.

'Meanwhile,' continued David, 'Come and meet people.' I do not remember all their names and who they were. Though there was the local Church of England vicar, a thin man in his forties with untidy grey hair and bad yellowy-brown stained teeth. There was his plumpish wife from Belfast who seemed to have a permanent smile on her face. There was one of David's colleagues from the local council with his shy smile from behind his horn-rimmed glasses, prematurely grey hair with matching coloured dandruff on the shoulders of his khaki summer jacket There was the local right-wing bore who thought half the government were 'bloody socialists' and wanted to have a re-run of the fall of France and the Battle of Britain. declined to be drawn. There were any number of young 'Young Conservatives', and there were some older 'Young Conservatives', and then there was Julia Roberts.

Julia Roberts was a woman of just forty. Her thick, straigh blond hair, cut just above her shoulders framed her fac beautifully. She smiled a lot revealing her flawless whit teeth. It was a kind, gentle, generous smile. She wa modest about her good looks probably due to he Protestant upbringing. She was wearing a sleeveless, flora summer dress cut well below the knee, but revealing good deal of her shoulders. David noticed me looking a her.

'Ah, she's dishy...she's very sweet,' he whispered into m ear. 'Come on, you can meet her.' He introduced me a Martin Braun, a journalist from Hamburg, 'who' interested in young Britons and their attitudes.' Slightl embarrassed, she said she was afraid she was slightly ou of that category. 'Rubbish,' reassured the host, putting a arm round her shoulders. Her green eyes lit up, 'Thank yo kind sir.' David politely disappeared leaving us alone. explained that I was interested in British life and politics i general and young people only in that I wanted to mee some for a possible article I was doing.

'Somehow you don't strike me as a Conservative,' I said rather foolishly and then trying to retrieve the situation went on, 'Of course, there's nothing wrong with being a Conservative like our host.'

She came to the rescue, 'I'm not really. I'm more of a Liberal. I voted Liberal last time, in '59 and before that. I've known David for some years and he is a near neighbour.'

Noticing her rings I asked about her husband who, she said, worked in the City. They had only one child, a boy called Martin. In addition to being attractive, she was easy to talk to and the conversation flowed. She asked me about my job, Hamburg and my family; I thought I saw slight relief and surprise when I explained I had never married. She had not been to Germany. She had loved holidays in France, Italy and Switzerland and had seen India as a child when her father worked there. She said she'd have to go soon because she had promised her husband not to be too late. He had not come because of his cricket interest. She wasn't interested in cricket. Her major hobby was painting and pottery. In a brilliant feat of improvisation, but without much confidence, I asked if she would like to see the preview of the Royal Academy's Summer Exhibition. Startled and confused by my offer, she flushed and replied somewhat hesitantly, 'Well, yes, I suppose it would be all right.' And then with greater confidence, she reaffirmed, 'Yes that would be nice.'

With Julia gone my interest in the garden party was rapidly waning. I decided to slip unobtrusively away five minutes or so after her. Just as I was about to take leave of my host, a new figure walked confidently from the French windows of the house and into the garden. His concession to summer was a light-blue, silky light-weight two-piece suit, but he still retained what I supposed was his old school tie. 'Ah good,' whispered David. And then loudly, 'Dickie. Hello, welcome!' Though I had studied 'The Times Guide to the House of Commons', I could not quite place Richard 'Dickie' Houghton-Smith. I knew he was not the local Member who was, of course, the Prime Minister, Harold Macmillan. As the steel-haired MP shook hands with his friend many of those present shyly took in the scene.

'How was Spain?' asked the host, his face revealing he already knew the answer. 'Excellent, excellent. I think we could learn a thing or two from Franco,' the MP said decisively.

'Dickie, let me introduce you to Martin Braun, a journalist from West Germany and, I think I can say, a friend.'

'Always glad to meet a friend of David's,' responded the MP politely taking my hand. David went to the house to produce a gin and tonic for his distinguished guest. After a few preliminaries the MP launched into a monologue, 'Shame about the war. We were taken for a ride all right. Who did it benefit? Your great nation is divided. Our empire is virtually at an end. America is pre-eminent and Communism has taken a third of the world. And we ostracise some of our true allies, Spain and South Africa. It just doesn't make sense. Anyway, if there's anything I can do for you, do please ring my office. I mean that! Here's my card.'

After ten minutes or so the MP moved on to mix with his ideological brethren avoiding one or two known 'One Nation' enthusiasts. 'Don't forget, Herr Braun,' he emphasised, 'ring me.'

'Dickie's a bit right-wing, but a wonderful chap,' David added in a half-whisper. 'And yes, do ring him and me too.' Then, with a sly wink, 'Hope you enjoyed yourself with Julia, you old devil! See you soon.' With that I took my leave and returned home.

24.

A very British institution

Even though I was just about on time, I felt guilty that Julia had arrived at the Royal Academy in Piccadilly five minutes before I did. She looked stunning and was again beautifully and tastefully attired. Nonetheless, she was clearly embarrassed to be out with a man other than her husband. We went through the rotating door and up the steps and then to the left to the ticket attendant. I caught her giving me an admiring look as I presented my card. I felt I had no right to be with such a trusting person. I think we made a handsome couple and certainly got many admiring glances from other visitors.

The selectors of the Royal Academy were often criticised for their narrow range of choices and their conservative attitude. For me, however, used only to Nazi art and 'Socialist Realism', the exhibition of 1963 was quite breathtaking. I must admit I did not understand it all, and I'm sure neither did Julia. What was The Common Market by William Roberts about? Even the portraits were not what most uninitiated viewers would expect. I liked best Hans Schwarz's, Miss Sian Phillips in the Duchess of Malfi. The Royal Academy seemed to be a very British institution and as I had imagined it as a child, and so, I was in no way disappointed. After the exhibits we went to the gallery bar. I offered Julia a drink and we both opted for Pimm's. For me this was another first and I guess Julia was not a regular Pimm's drinker either. She said she felt tipsy but happy on the second. After the exhibition we window-shopped in the Burlington Arcade and went for tea at Fortnum & Mason before taking the tube back to Victoria from where she caught her train to Bromley.

Before leaving, I asked her to go with me to the Royal Festival Hall for a concert. The guilt surfaced again but she knew she wanted to go with me. For her I was prepared to beg her to come and finally she conceded and said, 'Yes, you know I'd love to.' It was about two weeks before we next met. I managed to ring her once when her husband was not in. In the interim, I spent much of my time browsing in those wonderful bookshops along Charing Cross Road or in the Westminster public library coasting through *Hansard*, the official reports of the parliamentary debates. Although my main concern was recent developments, I could not help looking back to 1901 and finding the heated arguments in The Commons about the concentration camps in South Africa. So the substance of what I had heard in 1942 was true! There was Mr Dillon, MP for Mayo and a distant cousin of my mother, on 26

February, accusing the government of 'so barbarous a practice... capturing women and children by the thousand and detaining them as prisoners of war.' I had found another thing I loved about London: so much information freely available in books, shops and on the open shelves of libraries open to any member of the public who cared to avail themselves of it.

On the evening of my date with Julia I waited anxiously in the main entrance of the Festival Hall half expecting she would not come, but she did. At the interval she shyly took out a pair of glasses from her bag to read the programme. I tried not to appear surprised. To me she looked even cuter. We saw Sir John Barbirolli conduct the Hallé Orchestra in a programme of Haydn, Richard Strauss and Mahler's 4th - and all for 10 shillings each. Afterwards, as it was a very warm summer's evening, we lingered on the Embankment stopping for a drink and then strolling arm-in-arm along the river side chatting. It was wonderful. Surely these events were Britain at its best.

Solly had arranged for me to visit a newspaper in Manchester and so I could only see Julia briefly over the next week or so. As she was in London anyway to see her sister, I took her to Rules, one of London's oldest restaurants, just off the Strand in Covent Garden, for lunch. The clientele was a mixture of diplomatic, theatrical and political. She was impressed and pointed out Mickey Rooney, the American actor to me. I was more interested in the figure of Konni Zilliacus, the Labour MP for the

Gorton division of Manchester. As I was going there I asked him if I could call on him to get his view on things. He said he would be delighted. Julia was to meet her sister at Charing Cross station later and as we had time to spare I went with her. To her embarrassment her sister Cathy was already there. A mischievous grin spread across Cathy's face as Julia tried to introduce us.

In Manchester, Zilliacus took me on a tour of his constituency. He was a great linguist of Swedish/Finnish background, who had served as a British intelligence officer in the 1914-18 war. He insisted in speaking German and then Russian and, on hearing I spoke Spanish tried that as well. I denied any knowledge of any Scandinavian languages. He had little in common with his constituents and was more interested in international affairs than bread and butter issues. Much of his constituency was a vast slum and, although I had read about such conditions, it was a shock to physically see it, especially as it was not far from the fine shops and public buildings of the centre.

I said I would ring Julia, but despite ringing at times when she said she was likely to be alone, her husband picked up the phone on two occasions! On the third she did so only to put it down again immediately. I was very frustrated. I had to see her, so I drove down to Bromley one Wednesday morning. I knew of course that her husband would be away at work. With my heart pounding I knocked on the door of the detached mock-Tudor house, Holy Well. She opened it. I explained, 'I was just passing. I thought perhaps you'd offer me a cup of tea.' Once I'd said it I realised she might ask where I was going at this time and then I would have been flummoxed. Fortunately, she did not. She merely blushed and after a moment of confused joy, she replied, 'How lovely to see you Martin, of course, do come in.'

She had been in the middle of gardening. As we sat in the lounge sipping our tea we both knew it had to happen. The moment I touched her bare arm and then her cheek we had passed the 'point of no return'. We were both hungry for each other. After a few hugs and touches on the carpet, she said softly, 'Not here, let's go up stairs.' We spent several hours in the guest room. As I rode her, I cried, 'Julia, Julia, Julia, Darling Julia.' She gripped me as if her life depended on it and screamed with delight. Somehow the innocent are far more likely to be found out than 'professional' adulterers and Julia was no exception. She had forgotten that she had arranged for her friend, Margaret, to go round after lunch. After knocking several times at the door she reluctantly went home again. The trouble was my car was outside. What would Margaret think?

We agreed to meet again in central London at F&M the following week, but this time she did not turn up. I rang several times but either got no reply or the phone was put down. A week or so later I received a letter from her saying she could not go on. She loved me but felt too guilty and she could not abandon her son. I realised that she was right. What we had had, we would never forget it. If we went on I could only destroy her marriage. I could

174

not easily reveal my identity and ask her to go with me to East Germany. In *Death Takes A Holiday* the young woman goes off with Death but this was real life. Although difficult, I resisted the temptation to call her again. I was surprised that after such a brief relationship she had touched my emotions quite deeply. I felt like a jerk!

One other person I would have phoned if I could was my mother. I had sent her a card to our old address from Switzerland without, of course, putting any address on it. I attempted to find a telephone number for her but could not. I sent her a card from London just to re-assure her that I was in good health and that I was thinking of her. More I could not do without breaking all the elementary rules of security. It was frustrating.

25.

Profumo and Macmillan

Richard Houghton-Smith turned out to be as good as his word. He invited me for a drink in the House of Commons bar introducing me to several of his colleagues, including Sir Julian Ridsdale, MP for Harwich, who seemed more interested in Japan than Germany, and the old Etonian, Julian Amery, MP for Preston North, who with his financial interests was more interested in the British Empire than Europe. Amery was Minister for Aviation. Little did he know what a decisive influence his family had exercised over my life. It seemed these grand British families continued to 'serve' no matter what. Houghton-Smith also invited me to an evening 'at home' in his rather palatial house in Mayfair.

At the time, there was a lot of gossip flying around about possible changes in the government. There was also heated discussion about strikes of which a number were in progress in the car industry. I could sense both excitement and dismay about Soviet space achievements; the Soviets had just successfully launched the first woman into space. I was asked several times about whether President Kennedy was starting to rely more on the Germans than on the British. The mood was one of crisis.

Upon our arrival, Houghton-Smith introduced me to his wife, Elizabeth, a woman who clearly spent much time on her appearance and succeeded in her efforts. She had well-coiffeured, short grey hair, with lively, enquiring, grey-blue eyes and stood slender, almost gaunt in a silvery evening gown. The MP seemed to be testing me. 'Life's not all politics, is it, Herr Braun?' I readily agreed that this was my view too. 'You've not been married have you?'

'Sadly', I replied possibly even colouring a little, 'the girl I wanted did not want me, and since then I've been a bit adrift.'

'That's a shame, you poor man,' interjected his wife.

'But you don't play in the same league as Fox-Norris, I take it?'

'I'm sorry, I don't quite understand?' I enquired.

'Don't be so stupid darling, of course he doesn't,' said the hostess laughing nervously to defuse a potentially embarrassing situation.

'You know,' the MP pressed his point, 'isn't he a bit funny, a bit of an odd sort... er, queer?'

'That, I would not know.' I responded slightly shocked.

'Good, good, anyway like me you like girls. In that case, I'll invite you to another of our gatherings, this time in the country. They'll like a Nordic German type like you there.'

His wife nodded her approval, 'I'm sure Mr Braun will be a wonderful addition to our circle.'

The 'circle' gathered the following weekend in a country house in Hampshire not far from Portsmouth. I drove there abandoning the new, but very ordinary, Hillman Imp I had bought for £520 and hiring an up-market Jaguar for the weekend. I soon realised that this was no ordinary gathering. In social terms, it was a mixture of the county set, a few Conservative MPs, City business types, several naval officers from Portsmouth, some wives of the afore-mentioned, more mistresses, and a fairly large contingent of young women. Mrs Houghton-Smith welcomed me eagerly. We were immediately served glasses of champagne by a fairly short male figure dressed only in a Masonic apron and wearing a mask. Rather puzzled and startled by this apparition I gasped. Before I could thank him, Mrs Houghton-Smith, shrieked, 'Get away you dwarf, the other guests are waiting.' He thanked her and went on. 'He's one of Dickie's colleagues, you know, strange little man.'

'Hello, Bob,' rather dismissively she greeted the jovial, portly, Robert Boothby, MP, who had a girl on each arm. Then almost as an afterthought she shouted, 'Bob, are Jack and Christine not coming?'

'I don't think so dear lady,' replied Bob gravely. There was an all-night buffet which was serviced by tall, muscular, 'other ranks' from the nearby naval base. My first glimpse of Dickie was later by the side of the outside, heated swimming pool, where he was lounging around totally naked with two young girls, again totally naked. Another fellow, an MP from the North-West was looking rather hot, embarrassed and the worse for alcohol as he lay sprawled on some loungers with girls perched on both sides of him. Mrs Houghton-Smith led me into a dimly-lit, small hall from which *Fly Me To The Moon* was drifting out. There were very few people dancing but clearly she wanted to. We quick-stepped, we fox-trotted, we tangoed and we waltzed. She snuggled up to me and whispered, 'I've always loved you Nordic types, I like the way you carry yourself. You're confident but not beyond embarrassing. I could see you in SS uniform.' Did she know more about me than I thought? Briefly I was stunned by the comment, but thanks to the ambience my face gave nothing away. She led me through an adjoining room where the 'strange little man' was imprisoned in old stocks with his head and hands poking out. Two girls were seeing to it that he enjoyed himself as they cracked their whips across his back and buttocks. 'Just wait, you will yet whine like a dog beneath my whip,' threatened one, and then they simultaneously began to strike him again. The girls smiled as they drew back their whips, which hissed through the air. At first he winced. Then they let blow after blow rain down upon him. I couldn't believe what I was witnessing. 'That's a genuine 18th century punishment instrument,' Mrs Houghton-Smith announced proudly with a chuckle.

From the torture chamber we climbed up a wide staircase and along a wide corridor until we came to the end room. This was a large bedroom with a magnificent chandelier, a four poster bed, fine mirrors, a dressing table and a large ornate wardrobe, which was filled with uniforms of different periods and different armies. 'This one I think,' Elizabeth said with excitement, having thrown a cursory glance my way and run her finger along a number, then gone back to one already inspected. It was inevitably an SS uniform partly genuine and partly theatrical. 'Please,' she implored, 'do it for me.' As I put it on she undressed. She lay on the bed and on a nod from her I tied her hands and feet to the bed posts with the leather thongs placed there for the purpose. Clearly this was not her first time and she told me to 'spare no mercy and to it to me hard!' If the mirrors had been cameras what an album there would be! I told myself it was all in the line of duty and that my superiors in East Berlin would thoroughly approve. I mounted her and gave her what she wanted.

Only a week or so after my adventure in the 'circle' of the Houghton-Smiths, I realised who the hostess had missed on that night. John Profumo, Secretary of State for War, in the Macmillan government, had been forced to resign because of his relationship with Christine Keeler and her relationship with a Soviet intelligence officer. I had done my duty and gained very useful insights into the working of British society at the top, but I had not gained anything more than that.

Shortly after the downfall of Profumo, I received another phone call from Fox-Norris. He asked me about my encounters with the Houghton-Smiths and I gave him a sanitised version of events. He said he wanted to take me to meet some young people and felt sure I would enjoy myself. Curious about the event and about his sexual preferences, I agreed. We met in a pub near Oxford Circus underground at 8.30 one Wednesday evening. He explained that he was a member of a club where it was easy to pick up both British and foreign girls; was I game? Only a short distance away we found the Rheingold Club. It was a fairly plush, basement, night club frequented by men like ourselves seeking the company of women, in most cases considerably younger than we were. Many of them were au pair girls from Italy, Germany, Sweden and other West European states. I was soon buying Verena a drink. She was 23 and had worked as a secretary at Uetersen, a German air base near her native Hamburg. Now she was anxious to improve her English and was working as an au pair for a well-to-do family in Kensington. I could not believe my luck. I wined and dined her over the following three months. I told myself I would take it slowly and naturally. However, after a good meal at Rules on our third date she made sure she missed her last train from Waterloo. So it was a night-cap for two in a bar in Swiss Cottage. I had to work at the sexual side of our relationship for, although she was quite good looking, she was more of a housewife in the kitchen than a whore in the bedroom. It was not long before I had a great deal of information about the state of the West German air force as she had been there only a few months before. I did not push her to reveal state secrets. Most of them just fell into the long conversations we had, with her doing most of the talking; I helped her with her English, speaking in the language the whole time except when we made love. She was very grateful. By the time she was due to leave she had improved in all spheres. She had become somewhat obsessive and was ready to continue the friendship. She returned to her old post within the air force and we started writing and telephoning each other. I made fairly frequent trips to see her saying that although some of them were just for her, others were business trips which I had organised so that I could be with her. With her greatly improved standard of English she was promoted and the information continued to flow. After she had returned to Germany I tried one or two other girls at the Rheingold, but they were hardly likely to gain jobs which would have interested the Stasi.

In the winter of 1964, my position became less secure. To my surprise I got a phone call from Solly. He clearly resented the fact I had not been in touch for several months. I could hardly say no to an invitation to attend one of his discussion evenings. Macmillan had been forced to resign as Prime Minister in October and Labour, led by Harold Wilson, looked increasingly likely to win the forth-coming election. Solly and his friends wanted to have their say and send messages to the Labour leadership on what their priorities ought to be. After a rather unreal and sad debate, Solly brought out the Riesling, loyal as ever to the great Yugoslav Marshal. He then took me to one side. He had become an avid reader of all the publications to which I was supposed to be contributing. My published articles had been few and far between. It was obvious that he thought I had another role. I was only slightly relieved when he asked whether I was on 'secret work' for NATO or for some secret West German body like that bastard Gehlen. Although he hated Moscow for 'betraying Socialism' and being engaged in Russian imperialism, he had no time for General Gehlen, who now headed West German intelligence. He thought certain circles in Bonn were engaged in a policy of establishing German hegemony in Europe. If this was 'my game' I should have said. Speaking to him on a professional level, I attempted to re-assure him pointing out that much of journalism was simply gathering background material. He should have understood as he was, after all, a journalist, I emphasised, attempting to flatter him somewhat. As a 'backroom boy' he felt rather ill-used at Reuters; he never got a by-line. I really did feel sorry for him realising, however, that he could be a danger if he started to kick up a fuss, even though he was barking up the wrong tree. He had, or thought he had, contact with Colonel George Wigg, the Labour MP who had been so effective in bringing down Profumo. Wigg was not very friendly towards the West Germans. Perhaps my days in London were numbered.

After discussing my situation with my base, I received a signal to wind up my operation and return to East Berlin. Before I left I achieved one of my childhood ambitions. This was to attend a concert at the Royal Albert Hall. Charles Groves conducted the London Symphony Orchestra with Yehudi Menuhin and Mstislav

Rostropovich playing Brahms Concerto for Violin and Cello. Magic! It was very international and yet a very British evening. I had to reflect on the fact that although the Soviet Union had improved under Khrushchev some of its leading artists like Rostropovich preferred to live elsewhere.

26.

Adventures and misadventures in Bonn and Vienna

On my return to East Germany in the summer of 1964, I was debriefed by Hans Fruck, who congratulated me on the success of my mission. I resumed my old job, lived once again in my old flat and regained my former identity. Julia, Solly, David Fox-Norris, the Houghton-Smiths and all my other 'friends' seemed far away if not yet long ago. One person whom I was not allowed to forget was Verena. My bosses obliged me to keep up the relationship, although this was slightly more complicated operating from East Berlin. I started to make regular trips to see her in Hamburg claiming to have been in either Denmark or Sweden on business. The information continued to flow. On one occasion, when she was getting restless I took her for the weekend to Copenhagen, which was easy by train from Hamburg. We stayed at a good hotel, visited the famous Tivoli, danced to the Beatles' sounds, saw a - by then - old Ingmar Bergman movie Summer with Monika, and generally enjoyed ourselves. Naturally, I fulfilled all her requirements whilst there. She was very impressed by my Danish, I was impressed by Denmark.

On my next visit, Verena surprised me by asking my advice. She had the possibility of going to work in the Ministry of Defence in Bonn, but she was uncertain about this. Firstly, she would be moving away from family and friends. Secondly, she was worried about making it more difficult for me to see her, as it would mean an extra journey. Thirdly, she was not sure she would be up to the job. She took a good deal of persuasion to take the new post. I worked hard to re-assure her on the second and third points; as for the first, 'Bonn is not a million kilometres from Hamburg, is it?' I knew my superiors would be suitably impressed.

She was soon in Bonn in an office responsible for army-air force liaison. Where would it all end? We went on meeting regularly, sometimes in Bonn and other times, when she was seeing her relatives, in Hamburg. Problems developed for me in two directions however. We had been friends for just over two years and she was pressing me about a permanent bond, indeed marriage. Secondly, Fruck was getting greedy and wanted more systematic intelligence than could be gleaned from our lengthy, but necessarily fairly unstructured, conversations. I knew I could put her off for a time, but my senior colleagues in the HVA were less likely to be put off. Moreover, if I revealed myself as an East German intelligence officer I was sure the game would be up. I knew of other cases where women with no political views had been seduced into being Stasi spies. In fact, this was one of our major tactics – Romeo seducers. In this case I did not believe it would work. Another possibility, which I felt had a reasonable chance of success, was false flag recruitment. I could pose as a part-time intelligence officer from a neutral country like Sweden, Austria or Switzerland or, better still, as someone recruited by them to give a little help when and where I could. These were countries with good images. I could claim they had absolutely no interest in harming Western defence, but they wanted to know what NATO's plans were for an emergency. They were small countries which needed help to keep them free from domination by either side. My only problem was which country to choose. Sweden had its attractions, but from the language point of view Austria or Switzerland would be easier. In the end, it was decided by Fruck. We should go for Austria.

Over a candle-lit dinner in a discreet Bonn hostelry, I attempted to soften up Verena by expressing my worries about the way things were going in the West German state. The extreme right-wing, National Democratic Party, had gained entry into most of the regional parliaments, the opposition Social Democrats had joined a government headed by ex-Nazi party member, Kurt Georg-Kiesinger, any number of Nazis were being exposed having secured good jobs in the police, judiciary, the civil service and so on. Many of Germany's neighbours were very worried I suggested. She said she could understand their fears.

Without labouring the point too strongly, I switched tack and asked her would she like to spend a weekend with me in romantic Vienna. This was somewhere she had not been but I knew she craved to visit. She leapt at the offer.

Two weeks later, I picked up Verena in a new BMW 525 with all the trimmings, which I had hired for the trip. I had booked a comfortable hotel almost opposite St Stephen's Cathedral for a four night stay. After a night in which we worked hard to use up our sexual energies, and a day in the famous Vienna woods, we had dinner in the cultural quarter of Grinzing, followed by more love making, which that night seemed to hit new heights in the noise department. Perhaps, it was to do with the fact that we introduced some light bondage for the first time. There was a lot of moaning and groaning and screaming as if someone was in pain, but Verena seemed to be a more than willing student and was gaining in confidence sexually. I do remember some odd glances and furtive nudges the following morning when passing through reception.

In the delightfully ornate restaurant, I raised the question of meeting a 'friend of mine' over breakfast. Later during an early afternoon walk in the Hof Gardens, I 'confessed' how my friend had convinced me to give him a little help from time to time, presenting him as a member of the Austrian secret service. He badly wanted to meet Verena, without of course any obligations. Presently, we met 'Erich' in one of Vienna's many coffee houses. He was a Curd Jürgens type. He had been chosen for his mature good looks and style.

He easily put me into the shade as a gentleman. In appearance he resembled a slightly old-style, Austrian officer. He was, in fact, an Austrian recruited by the Stasi. After two hours of 'Erich's' charm offensive, Verena decided she would help world peace by delivering material to me for dispatch to 'Erich'. That evening we confirmed our three-way friendship over champagne and caviar in an elegant, but discrete restaurant. We took several pictures of each other as souvenirs. On our last day in the 'Waltz Capital', we met our friend in his 'office' where Verena refined her considerable photography skills. I watched her practice micro-photography and I could see she was rather enjoying her new little adventure. Before we left, 'Erich' gave both Verena and me envelopes bearing our names, 'Just in case you have any expenses.' I sought to gradually switch Verena's attention from me to 'Erich'. I did so by praising him as an interesting and mysterious figure, running myself down somewhat, missing our dates on two occasions and ensuring that Verena and 'Erich' met at more frequent intervals. He visited Bonn several times; she went to Vienna, all expenses paid. 'Erich' was ordered to take the slow road to seduction and it was a year later, after a gradual build-up of interest, that he got her into his bed on one of her weekends in Vienna. It was just in the nick of time.

The author John Le Carré called Bonn 'A small town in Germany' and this it certainly was in the 1960s and 1970s. Before being declared the provisional seat of government in 1949, it was only known for its connection with

Beethoven. A university town, it was also a place where some who worked in the large city of Cologne retreated to. Despite the growth of government and other employment in Bonn, the building of new ministries, the headquarters of the political parties, the foreign embassies, the offices of lobbyists and interest groups, it remained essentially a small town. Its rail and bus stations remained ludicrously inadequate. It must be admitted, this was also its charm. It had a more intimate atmosphere than most other capitals and was less intimidating. This could also be a drawback for someone with a borrowed identity, for those attempting illicit sexual liaisons or for those attempting to break-off relations with someone. Sooner or later you would bump into each other on one of the narrow Bonn streets or alleys. Fate struck in my case in April 1970.

As I walked one day along Beethoven Gasse, a rather ponderous uniformed female figure came towards me. There was something familiar about her but I couldn't put my finger on it. Then it dawned on me. It had been about 17 years since that night of celebration which had ended in our arrest. It was Helga! She passed me without saying anything and then we both turned simultaneously.

'Martin? Is that you Martin?'

'Helga, after all this time... What a surprise! You're still fond of uniforms I see.' She tried to smile at this embarrassed comment.

'It's a job, it's a job,' she sighed, her words coming out almost in a lament. She was a traffic warden and her uniform was slightly too small, which gave her a slightly tarty appearance. On the other hand, I could not help thinking of Miss Norris with her clean and stiff appearance. As Helga was on duty, we arranged to meet in a Croat restaurant two streets away after she finished her shift. She told me her story, how she had been severely beaten, transferred to the notorious Waldheim Prison, but had been released by the mob on 18 June 1953. She had lost no time leaving East Germany for the West where she had remained ever since. At first she had stayed with her brother who had never returned to East Berlin after the war. I explained I knew nothing of the revolt which freed her, having been kept isolated from the world at that time. I told how I had been able to resume my duties in the People's Police, but I then went on to fabricate the rest of my journey through life. I claimed that I had retired from the People's Police to become an editor with a publishing company. I was now on a business trip in West Germany. Unfortunately, I'd be leaving soon. Sadly, she looked a wreck. I did not feel I looked quite so old as she did. I was 44 and she was now about 47, but looked a good deal older. She had not found it easy to settle down in the West and had never married. I explained that I was married - a slight distortion of the truth - but I felt it necessary. We both knew there was no going back. After the meal I took her to the underground and gave her a good-bye kiss on the cheek wishing her 'All the best.' In the end, I was glad I had bumped into her as I had often thought about her, felt guilty, and hoped that she was well. I was convinced she did not know my true reason for being in Bonn. It was obvious, however, that I could not keep turning up in

Bonn. Sooner or later we would meet again, and again, and again. I cut my visits to Bonn, seeing Verena less and less; occasionally in Hamburg and another time in Vienna. It was in the Austrian capital that, on 'Erich's' urging, Verena confessed her relationship with 'Erich' to me. We had just been to see Gottfried von Einem's opera, *Der Besuch der alten Dame*, (The Old Lady's Visit), a tale of corruption if ever there was one, when we agreed it was better if we parted. By then, she was confirmed in her new relationship. 'Whatever happened to romantic love?' I could not help thinking on my way back to my lonely hotel room.

It would be silly of me to pretend I did not miss Verena or had no feelings for her after all the years of our friendship (1964-1971). I would have to be have been totally heartless and without emotion and that wasn't me. I did miss her. I had put little effort into finding myself a genuine partner in those years, although I had not had that many real opportunities to do so. Soon, however, my luck appeared to change.

27.

From Tehran, Pari

As the 'fight for peace' and the campaign for the recognition of our German Democratic Republic accelerated over the 1960s and early 1970s so did my workload. I had to vet, as best I could, British visitors to the Republic. These were still mainly businessmen or 'peace friends'. This work brought me more and more into contact with the *Friedensrat* (Peace Council). I stayed in the background most of the time so as not to blow my cover. But for the times when I had to, or wanted to, mix with the guests, I was given the cover of being an editor at a fairly obscure publishing house. The *Friedensrat* was well provided for with funds and put on any number of seminars for participants from a large number of countries. Sometimes they would attempt to have participants from several countries present; on other occasions, they received 'delegations' from just one country.

On one such occasion in April 1971, ex-Major Dr Egbe Frankenberg und Proschiltz was present. He had made name for himself since 1945 as a political-milita commentator, friendly to the Soviet Union. Some thoug he was just a collaborator of the Soviet Security Servic the KGB. He clearly recognised me from our infreque meetings at the League of German Officers and fro Moscow, but believed neither of us would want to reminded of those days. I took his lead and said nothir and, after a few polite references to his publications, le him talking to a West German neutralist. I worked my wa through trade unionists from Glasgow, Manchester ar Newcastle, through a writer from London, who wa obscure and was to remain so, congratulated Profess Stefan Doernberg, on his new book, a short history of th Republic, and exchanged a few words with Herma Budzislawski, a professor of journalism and a *Friedensr* regular, who was standing with Kurt Goldstein from th Berlin radio, also a *Friedensrat* regular. Goldstein ha survived the Spanish Civil War and Auschwitz. John Pe the British journalist and KGB agent, waved as he talked a gentleman of the cloth from Coventry, but before I cou say hello to him, Frau Lieselotte Otting, now a leadir member of our 'Liberal Democratic Party', formerly enthusiastic member of Hitler's party, grabbed me. Sl wanted to introduce me to Pari Alavi, who worked for tl Democratic Women's League (DFD).

Pari Alavi was a member of the Iranian People's Par (Communists), which had been banned by the Shah. Tho f its members, who had been fortunate enough to escape, ived mainly in our Republic, in Bulgaria or in Soviet Azerbaijan. Aged 35, Pari was already a widow, her husband having been killed by the Shah's dreaded secret police, the *Savak*. She was an accomplished linguist speaking fluent German, Russian and English in addition o Persian and, from her mother's side Turkish. Frau Otting, who in another life had sponsored Himmler's SS breeding project, thought we would have lots in common as I was known too as a linguist and an expert on English and Britain. Pari was a woman of passion and intellect, both qualities of which attracted me, and dressed in a much more feminine and fashionable way than most of our 'emancipated' German comrades. It also helped that she was very beautiful. She was of medium height and of slender build with incredible dark brown eyes, which were always full of life. They were like a gateway into her soul. Her thick, glossy black hair contrasted well with her, well-cut, discreet, yellow dress. Before I had considered the position, I was asking for her telephone number which she readily gave.

To my surprise it was Pari who made the first contact after the Peace Council meeting. She rang me to invite me to a reception for the publication of a German translation of a novel by the Iranian writer, Professor Bezorg Alavi, who also lived in East Berlin. My other surprise was that many of those present were the same *Friedensrat* crowd, including Buzislawski, Goldstein and Peet. Peet, who was either about to get divorced or had just done so, made it

obvious that he was more interested in Pari than in he
namesake, who was no relation. He did not succeed and w
left together and remained together marrying the followin;
year. Shortly after that, Pari gave me a son, Heinrich (afte
Heinrich Heine), Bezorg (after the writer).

Married life had its ups and downs. Even before we go
married there were problems. My superiors took a dir
view of me 'marrying out', even to a comrade from
fraternal party. Pari had a Soviet passport dating from he
first years of exile. This could have caused problems bu
did not. Sex was never a problem even though Pari wa
used to men who had been circumcised and was brought u;
with the belief that this was cleaner. Life in the Germa
Democratic Republic was a problem. Firstly, there was th
geographical location. In Berlin, the weather can b
gloomy for long periods with grey skies. This ofte
depresses those not used to it. Secondly, housing was
problem. My flat was just about big enough to house tw
young newly-weds without belongings. It was difficult fo
us, particularly after the birth of our son. Later we got
second flat on the same floor in our block, the tenants o
which had left for West Germany. Thirdly, it can be
strain not being able to use your own native language ver
much. Fourthly, the lack of an extended family can caus
loneliness, especially in a country where people ar
naturally reserved. The situation in the Republic mad
people even more reserved. People in the block of flat
where we lived rarely had much to do with each othe
outside special occasions when they were obliged to com

together as tenants and, as citizens of the German Democratic Republic, had to 'celebrate' election day, the founding of the Republic and similar events. Pari had hoped for more from Socialism. Our respective jobs also took a heavy toll on our marriage and our lives. Pari was expected to travel a great deal for the DFD, not only in the Socialist Camp, but also to Austria, Finland and Switzerland. I had to put in long hours at the Ministry. We both would have liked to see the world together, but we could not do this for practical as well as political reasons. We did manage some beautiful times together in Prague, Budapest and on the Black Sea. Finally, we both had meetings of our respective workers' parties, Tudeh and SED, as well as our other obligations.

My biggest problem was to tell my partner who I was and what I did. She had fallen for a German in a responsible literary position - or so she thought. It was a shock for her to learn of my true profession. It was difficult for her to understand that I was not a 'secret policeman' but an intelligence officer 'fighting for peace', fighting to prevent war. She also wanted to know about my wartime activities and they were as difficult to discuss. Only those who have been in such an appalling position can fully understand it. I could not, in the circumstances bring myself to confess to her that I was not really German. She often said half-jokingly that I was not German; there must have been a mistake in the hospital when I was born. She felt it, it was her gut feeling. My German was too perfect and without strong regional accent, but it was not really that, she

believed my temperament was not German. I believ
unfairly, she thought I was too kind and sensitive to b
German. This was certainly not my view of the Germans
They are a mixed bunch like all other nations.

We had political differences too. The removal o
Khrushchev in October 1964 was a shock, although littl
changed. The same was true in May 1971 when Ulbrich
was replaced by Honecker. Could the Socialist Camp no
change its leaders without a palace coup? By contrast, i
Bonn the Christian Democrats lost office in 1969 afte
twenty years to be replaced by Willy Brandt's Socia
Democrats without any crisis in the state. Pari regarded th
Brandt government as progressive and she was far mor
critical than I about conditions in the Socialist Camp. Sh
soon became what was in 1976 called a 'Euro
Communist', opposing the Democratic Centralist structur
of party control. It's fair to say she dragged me along wit
her. She had friends in Prague and was up in arms over th
Warsaw Pact invasion of the country in 1968 and th
overthrow of the Czechoslovak Communist Part
leadership. Some of us in the Ministry thought it was a ba
move too.

As the years went by we enjoyed our lives together, but w
would have enjoyed them more had we been less sensitiv
about the world around us.

28.

Death in Iran

One day in the spring of 1978 I got news, through an internal document, of a big security exercise in Berlin. I could hardly believe it when I got more details. The Shah of Iran was going to pay a state visit to the German Democratic Republic. In a minor way, it was like Soviet Foreign Minister Molotov going to see Hitler! Our media had poured scorn on the Shah for decades as a lackey of Imperialism, and torturer and murderer of Iranian patriots. Now, he was to receive all the pomp and ceremony we could throw at him to flatter his considerable vanity. It was rumoured one plane would be needed just for the wardrobe of the royal couple. He and his wife were both to receive honorary doctorates from the Humboldt University of Berlin. The émigré Tudeh Party would have to keep a low profile, though there was no question of handing over wanted Iranians to the Shah's secret police, the notorious, American-trained, Savak. Dr Fichtner, an expert on Iran at the Humboldt University, and one of the few East Germans to have visited the country, was actually predicting serious disturbances in the Shah's 'Empire', with even the possibility of his overthrow. I had known him slightly since we were both prisoners in Russia and met him occasionally at Iranian cultural events. His views were discounted as he was not even an SED comrade. As for the Iranians in the Republic, they were sickened and dismayed by the proposed visit, Pari amongst them.

'Why had the SED once again decided to pursue such an opportunist policy?' Pari asked me rhetorically. She knew the answer as well as I did. She also knew I had nothing to do with it. Iran was located in a totally separate department of the Ministry for State Security. The answer was our Republic needed cheap oil and Iran could provide it. It was simple economics. The Shah would drive a hard bargain though and this meant the Tudeh Party's activities would be greatly curtailed. The other reason was that Honecker and his colleagues in the Politburo, the leading organ of our Party, still suffered from an inferiority complex. They felt they needed all the recognition, prestige and glamour they could get to convince their people that they were really legitimate. It was a case of saying to the East German people, 'If the USA, Britain, France, the Soviet Union, West Germany, the Emperor of Japan and even the Shah of Iran, recognise us, why won't you?' Like the Shah, there was nothing Honecker loved more than going on a state visit. These two men, who had started so very differently in life, were ending up extremely similar. Western liberals had some sympathy for Honecker as the underdog, the working class hero who had spent 10 years in Nazi jails. Honecker, like the Shah, pursued the cult of personality. At the time of the Leipzig Fair, there would be 30 photographs of him on eight papers of a single issue of *Neues Deutschland*.

The degree parchments were ready for the royal couple at the Humboldt University - but the Shah never came. The couple had to amend their travel itinerary. The people of Iran had arisen and they were being thrown out. In January 1979, the Shah and his wife fled Iran. No one seemed to know who was behind it. It appeared to be what we called a genuine 'national bourgeois revolution'. The various opposition groups were calling for a republic similar to that of France. In this situation, the Tudeh Party called on all its members to do their duty where ever they were. What did that mean? A considerable portion of them were ordered to return to their homeland in an attempt to exercise influence on the direction of the revolution. I dreaded to think what this meant for my own family. For days, even weeks, we skirted round the subject; we attempted to avoid the issue; it was like walking on eggshells at times because of the tension. It had been part of our marriage agreement that I would understand if the situation in Iran changed in such a way as to enable her to play her part in the political life of her homeland. But I guess, deep down, I did not think this day would come so quickly. She now believed the time had come and, in any case, she had to follow party discipline. I argued that the Tudeh Party appeared to have little influence in Iran. There were few cadres in the country and most of those outside it could not understand the true situation. I also believed that the US would not stand idly by and allow Iran to, at best, sink into chaos, and at worst, allow a hostile regime to take over. They had intervened in 1952-3 and they would do so again. It would be a terrible waste of lives if people went back with false illusions. One other factor was that the Tudeh Party itself was divided. There were those who still followed Moscow, and there were the Euro-Communists, like Pari, who were for an Independent Iran, feeling its way to Socialism on the basis of the experiences of the working class movements in other parts of the so-called Third World and Western Europe. There were also others who tended towards Trotskyism or Maoism. I knew such internal party conflicts could be very bitter, even deadly. In this situation, Pari had to fear not only the Shah's agents but also some of her own comrades.

The telephone calls from Iranian friends, acquaintances and party comrades became more frequent and more urgent. I knew I was fighting a losing battle. Pari felt it was her *Schicksal*, *Sarivesht* - her destiny - to return and do what she could for her struggling people, who had shown such courage against seemingly impossible odds. The Shah had demonstrated that the secret police, informers and massive armaments were no match for a people aroused. It was a warning to all tyrants whatever they called themselves. Via West Germany, she took a plane for Tehran, our son and I could not hold back the tears. On the airport at Frankfurt, someone was playing Rod Stewart, 'I m sailing... to be near where you are.' We attempted to oke saying that when she was in the government we would expect an invitation to stay at the Tehran Hilton. I had the underlying feeling of loss; one way or another, things would never be the same again.

We followed the events in Iran more closely than ever and it soon became clear that the Tudeh Party, which in the 1940s had been important, was no longer so. A new force had been growing up, which was based not on Marxism but on the Iranian version of Islam. It was led by the religious leader, Ayatollah Khomeini, who outwitted his allies as well as his enemies. He built up a broad anti-Shah coalition which the Tudeh Party decided to join. On 31 March 1979, Khomeini felt strong enough to proclaim an Islamic Republic. Heads started to roll. Not just the former Shah officials faced execution, but thousands who had helped the revolution to prevail were either shot or beheaded, the majority without trial. It was reported that in some towns and cities the roads actually ran red with the blood of the dead. Armed Islamic gangs turned on Leftists. Arson was used against the homes, offices and other properties of Left-wing groups just as it had been against the Shah. It was in one such attack that Pari perished.

We had tried to keep in touch by letter and by phone, but this became increasingly difficult as the revolution in Iran intensified. Pari did not have much time to write, and telephoning East Berlin could take hours, but one way or another messages got through fairly frequently, if not regularly. It was not easy for me to use the normal link from East Berlin. In January 1979, the whole of the Stasi was thrown into a panic by the defection of Lieutenant Stiller to the West. He had been in the HVA though thankfully, not in my department. It later transpired that he had been working for West German intelligence for two and a half years. As a result of his defection, 16 Stasi agents were arrested in West Germany. This meant heightened security and investigations in our headquarters which in turn made it more difficult to communicate with anyone abroad even though, in my case, my superiors knew all about my wife.

After April 1979, all communication with Pari ceased. I attempted, through my remaining Iranian contacts in Berlin, to find out where Pari was and how she was. It was a month after the event that I heard the devastating news – she had been killed when an Islamic mob had stormed the bookshop she managed. It was no consolation to me that I had expected a tragedy of this kind. Upon hearing the news I felt that someone had kicked me in the stomach and head simultaneously. My head was spinning and my mind confused. I could not believe I would never see her again. Once it sank in, I was left with a massive chasm, a feeling of emptiness. She had remained true to her ideals and her country to the end, but Iran had merely exchanged one tyranny for another. As for me, at 53, I was lonely and alone again. Since Pari's departure our son was being brought up by his Iranian aunt and her German husband in

Dresden. I could not but quote the Persian mathematician and philosopher, Omar Khayyam, to myself:

> There was a door to which I found no key.
> There was a veil past which I could not see.
> Some little talk awhile of me and thee,
> There seemed - and then no more of thee and me.

I just played a tape of Henryk Gorecki's Third Symphony and wept uncontrollably.

29.

A new Man in Moscow, 1985

'You and I go a long way back, Comrade. I knew you would make it,' said Comrade General Mielke. It was 1986; I had been promoted at last on my sixtieth birthday. I was now Colonel Martin Thomas. Several other comrades received their commander's praise and congratulations on their promotion that day. We all drank the customary glass of *Sekt* and nibbled at the light buffet which our chieftain had provided. The head of the HVA, Deputy Minister, Comrade General Markus Wolf, was also present but took little part in the festivities. General-Secretary Comrade Honecker was not present either, as he had a health problem, but we were assured he was with us in spirit, and he gave us his full blessing from above, gazing at us from a large portrait on the wall. The whole reception was rather formal and stiff, flavoured with a touch of jealousy here and there. I was not sorry to slip away and disappear down the underground and head for 'home'. A muddled version of Yoko Ono's *Give Me Something*, went through my head, 'The food is cold, Your eyes are cold, The window's cold, The bed's cold, Give me something that's not cold, come on, come on...'

Not long after my promotion, on a May morning in 1986, I was changing underground trains at Alexanderplatz, when on the platform I noticed a tall, lean, slightly bent figure. He had a thin face and a long white beard like an Old Testament prophet. I knew him, but I could not quite place him. Eventually, I realised it was John Peet. When he looked in my direction, he smiled, and said, 'How goes it? Still in the fight for peace, comrade?' Knowing Peet a little, I took this as a good natured, rhetorical question, which at the same time, was laden with doubt. We had not met for at least two years so I invited him for a drink in a cafe on Rosa-Luxemburg-Platz.

As we sat there he explained he was, 'Bloody well, pissed off with life.' Perhaps, somewhat cynically, I presumed he was just having some domestic bother with his fourth wife. He assured me that was not the case. He did not like what he called the 'benevolent paternalism' of the SED leadership and the endless bureaucracy in the Republic. He had become a 'Gorby' man. I cautiously agreed that we needed some of Gorbachev's ideas in Berlin. And then he rather startled me by saying, 'You know, I always thought you were some sort of Brit.' It took me a second or two to regain my composure. I then commented. 'I take that as a complement.' We parted amicably. I did not see Peet again. He died of cancer in 1988 aged 73.

I cannot say my meeting with Peet cheered me up. I to
was 'pissed off' with the way things were going; I was als
'pissed off' with being over 60. I did not feel old an
physically I was in good shape. I still idealised the amazing
Czech athlete, Emil Zatopek and ran or biked nearly ever
day, but the damned clock kept ticking! One day, I wa
assigned to 'hold the hand' of 'Diana'. I thought to mysel
'I bet she's no way like the Diana.' I knew we had a Diana
my colleague Rosier had spoken to me about her at some
point, but I had not met her nor had I taken down the
details of her appearance. She was an English woma
recruited on a trip to Leipzig. As an analyst rather than a
field officer, I seldom actually met our agents. 'Diana
Diana, Diana,' I must admit, I thought and fantasised abou
her quite a lot in the days before our *Treff*. This was to be
at the Palast Hotel, one of the Republic's finest, in the
centre of East Berlin, overlooking the water. Would she be
tall or would she be short? Would she be slender o
rotund? Would she be blond, brunette or even a red head
Would she be a dull academic or a lively free spirit? For a
second I thought, 'Could she be ethnic?' I realised that wa
nonsense because that would have been underlined and I
might have noticed that. I knew her motives were
apparently a mixture of ideology and adventure lust. Well,
I fully understood both. On the appointed day, I arrived
early but went off to the washroom to check my
appearance as well as relieve my bladder, before she
arrived. I then took up my position armed, as instructed,
with a copy of the literary magazine, *Weimarer Beiträge*,
and in that a plain envelope with a contribution to her

'expenses'. I sat waiting in the lobby of the hotel. She was late. It was the privilege of a lady to be late; she knew Berlin but not all that well and had perhaps underestimated the time she needed. After a few minutes, I got up and walked around the considerable foyer. There was, after all, more than one entrance. Not seeing anyone who even vaguely came into her category, I resumed my seat. After 20 minutes, I thought, 'The fools have given me the wrong hotel.' Presently, the receptionists changed shift. After 30 minutes of sitting, looking rather silly so I thought, I asked myself, 'What if she has got disillusioned, or has just got cold feet, and is not coming?' Five minutes later, a receptionist came over and asked, 'Are you Herr Braun?' I nodded. 'I'm very sorry,' he continued, 'I've just come on duty, and found a note which you should have received 45 minutes ago. I'm really very sorry. The person you are expecting to meet cannot come. She will be in touch.' For once I had a strong drink and left the Palast, bitterly disappointed and depressed. I knew I was being foolish, after all, this was not a proper date, indeed, not a date at all. It was just a business meeting. I could not help myself. However, I did have cause to be depressed about far more important matters.

In April 1986, the XI Congress of the SED was held in East Berlin. It was a great disappointment to me and others like me. Our boss, the 79-year-old Comrade Mielke, followed the example of his boss, Erich Honecker, 74, and decided to stay on as Minister for State Security. All the other members of the SED leadership followed them.

Could these old, and in some cases very old men, some of them sick, solve the increasing problems of the German Democratic Republic? It seemed highly unlikely, despite all the medical attention they received. Yet Honecker decided to announce his last, mad, gamble. He wanted to turn the Republic into a world leader in micro-chip production and information technology. After his fall from power, one of his colleagues claimed they were trying to 're-invent the wheel'. It meant everything. All the reserves of the Republic were to be thrown at this project. In the Ministry, technological espionage was to be stepped up. One other blow, which came later in the year, was the resignation of the head of the HVA, the notoriously illusive and camera shy, Markus Wolf. I had only met Wolf, who was a legend, a few times. If he was vain, he had much to be vain about. He had built up the HVA to the successful body that it had become. He was a charming and erudite man. Rumours abounded about his departure. He was ill, he had fallen out with Honecker, he had fallen foul of Mielke because of his womanising, he wanted to devote himself to writing, he wanted to attempt to mobilise those elements in the Party who favoured Gorbachevian reforms. Any and all of these rumours could have been true. He certainly had excellent ties with Moscow and was a fluent Russian speaker.

If Wolf was attempting to use his influence in the direction of reform there was no evidence of success. On the contrary, the men around Honecker and Mielke were determined to keep things as they were. Kurt Hager, the

SED's chief ideologue, interviewed by *Stern*, April 1987 remarked, 'If your neighbour changed the wallpaper in his flat, would you feel obliged to do the same?' In other words, you can forget reforms! Our leaders fiddled while Rome burned. Embryo opposition groups were forming, more people were applying for exit visas to go West and the economy was showing signs of severe strains and dislocations as Honecker's crazy IT scheme greedily gobbled up our investments. In the same year, however, there was a sign of hope. Honecker went to Bonn in September with Gorby's blessing. West German political and business leaders seemed to be falling over each other to receive him. His peace offering was the announcement that the (rarely used) death penalty had been abolished in our Republic. We hoped secret negotiations would lead to better relations between East and West Germany and to reforms within our Republic.

30.

At a Conference in Leipzig, 1988

Encouraged by the Party, Leipzig University was increasingly active in attempting to improve its international profile and attract trading partners to the Republic. As the languages spoken other than German were English and Russian, and some of the guests were of the top rank, I was delegated, once or twice, to keep an eye on the security arrangements. In June 1988, I was asked to step in once again at a conference on 'Non-Material Exports'.

As usual I walked from the huge, cavernous, railway station across the centre of town to make my call at the Ministry's Leipzig headquarters, the so-called 'round comer' on the Dittrichring. The facade was that of a magnificent nineteenth-century merchant's palace, while inside it had been partly rebuilt into a vast bunker, the ground floor of which was windowless. On the roof, seven storeys up, were any number of radio antennae which linked it to the rest of Mielke's empire across the Republic. I did not know the building well, but I knew that within it sat operatives who together could listen to up to 2,000 telephone calls at a time. In another part of the building, the 120 colleagues of Department 'M' were busy opening mail with gloved hands. They cleared between 1,500 and 2,000 letters a day. Typical of the confiscated items would be a letter from a mother to Honecker complaining about her son's army posting, a letter from a student to an American acquaintance asking for a guide book to Boston, a letter from a teacher protesting to the Chinese Embassy about a death sentence in Shanghai, a letter from a 12-year-old girl to a Swedish pop group asking for a signed photograph and an unsigned letter of solidarity to the dissident writer Stephan Heym. I had once lost my way and had ended up in one of the cellars, a place so cold and un-inviting I would not want to venture there again, but where the guards bunked down in fairly squalid conditions.

I had to check the list of conference participants against my own list and read any additional material they thought I ought to see. Somewhere in the labyrinth of offices I found the duty sergeant sitting in his little office looking bored, surrounded by beautiful, naked girls, which to his frustration were only posters on the office walls. Before leaving the building, I paid a courtesy call on General Manfred Hummitzsch, who as usual formally welcomed me into his empire. Three years younger than me, Hummitzsch had done well, which was more remarkable because he had no Soviet background and had spent most of his life in Leipzig advancing his career in that city. I knew he owed much of his success to being the opposite of me. For years, I had believed that if you were good at your job, your achievements and dedication would be recognised. He, on the other hand, realised that you had to be a complete conformist who built up friendships and ties exclusively within the Stasi and within the SED; job competence and job satisfaction came a long way behind.

The conference participants came from the USA, the Soviet Union, People's Republic of China, Finland, Hungary, Poland and the United Kingdom. In addition, there were a considerable number from both East and West Germany including Heinz Ruhnau, head of the West German airline Lufthansa, and Professor Kurt Biedenkopf, the well-known West German Christian Democratic politician and, some said, future Chancellor. As usual, most of the guests were in the Interhotel Merkur on the Gerber Straße. This was a five star luxury hotel, which towered above the surrounding buildings. Western-built, it was a symbol of the international status of the German Democratic Republic and of the good times to come. However, in this palace of a hotel, only convertible currency could be used. This meant it was effectively closed to all but a tiny handful of East Germans. From the Stasi point of view its modernity meant it was easier to install video cameras into the rooms. As on the second day of the conference I visited our video room, where I found a young colleague tittering and slapping his thighs as he watched a naked, Japanese businessman, wrestle with two of our girls young enough to be his grand-daughters. When he saw me he tried to pull himself together but I told him to relax. It was funny, revolting and sad, all at the same time. In a second room a Dutch guest was relieving himself with, what I hoped were his wife's knickers, while in a third, a forty-something American woman tourist executive was just stepping naked from the bathroom to get a smoke. On the fourth monitor I saw an elderly West German woman sat staring into space. I knew she had come to visit the grave of her brother having missed his funeral the week before due to a mix-up over her visa. I ordered the video controller to turn off the second, third and fourth cameras. He apologised saying they had been aimed at the previous occupants. The Japanese gentleman, however, was a big fish who could be a serious investor.

The whole video theatre made me think about my own life and activities; the businessman was only slightly older than myself. In a, for me, quiet moment when the conferencees were in full flood with Ruhnau, a Social Democrat, eloquently defending Biedenkopf from a young West German Leftist, I left the university and made my way by taxi to the Russian Church with its magnificent golden dome. There, I lit a candle for Alexandra and another for Tari and a third one for my mother. Perhaps, I was just getting old, soft and sentimental. But the gesture relieved my emotions slightly. On my way back I walked through the decaying Jugendstil streets of Leipzig, a great city which was still only a shadow of what it had been in, say, 1913. Leipzig, shabby, dirty and crumbling had become more East Europe than Central or West Europe. As was my habit, I walked far more than I needed to. Many of the streets had big names like -Mahler, Mendelssohn, Wagner Tschaikowski, memorialising the city's great musical heritage and tradition, but their shabbiness was an insult to the great composers whose names they bore. Gustav Mahler-Strasse was home to one of the Ministry's largest Leipzig buildings.

It was on the Tschaikowskistraße that the only English participant at the conference stopped me to ask the way. I asked if he were English or American. His German was, as I assured him, excellent, but he had an Anglo-American accent. Of course, I knew him but he did not know me. Given my emotional state, I made the mistake, if that's what it was, that so many spies had made before me. In a moment of weakness they confessed without any need to do so. They had reached a certain state of being 'burnt out', of weariness, of despair or even of wanting to cause excitement. Atom spy, Klaus Fuchs did this, so did our man in Bonn, Günter Guillaume. In my case, this meant I could not help mentioning to the Professor that I was English. We talked as we walked and paused for 30 minutes to chat over a coffee in the fine old Madler Passage. As the evening was closing in, I invited him to a meal at the well-known Falstaff restaurant. When I thought about it, he was, apart from John Peet, one of the very few English people I had really spoken to in the last 24 years. What a crazy situation! He knew our situation quite well, in fact very well, for an outsider. I considered this was perhaps the main reason why he had a Stasi banning order hanging over his head. This, of course, he did not know, but I knew from a study of his file. I was glad I did not have to deal with his type of case. Defence against external threats from political deviationist elements was not part of my brief. His cheerful, sympathetic manner, and my curiosity about him, basically why any Englishman should get involved in the study of the Republic, led us from one bottle of Bulgarian red wine to another. His first visit to our Republic was to the World Youth Festival of 1951, when I was already a war veteran and he still a school boy. I remembered it well. Another surprise was that he had been located in a school in Mahlsdorf. I did not mention that I was there too, nor what I had been doing. He mentioned the name Rudolf Buchwald. I vaguely remembered the former paratrooper and People's Police colleague but did not admit this. Soon I found myself talking about the war years and my involvement 'on the wrong side'. What drew me to the Englishman was his knowledge and the fact he tried to understand the human dilemma. He was not quick to judge, and take a clichéd view of peoples, groups, situations or above all individuals. It was after midnight when we left the restaurant, the staff had been getting restless, but as they had an idea what my job was likely to be, they did not disturb us. Nonetheless, I felt obliged to leave a good tip. I assured the Professor that he could get in touch with me via a friend in the Leipzig tourist office. I would be pleased to hear from him. A postcard from Nottingham, ancient city of Robin Hood and more recently Nottingham Forest football club, would be welcome. If he had a spare copy of one of his works, so much the better. We said good-bye at the entrance to his hotel, the Merkur. I knew he would not be wrestling with anyone that night, nor would I. He knew me as a 'kind of literary editor', retired language teacher, who still did the odd job for the Leipzig Tourist Board.

31.

Talent-spotting in Southern California

M_y internal flight from San Francisco arrived late into Long Beach airport and the ensuing rush hour traffic jam ensured that I arrived later still. When I finally made it to the conference on 'The Two German States at Forty', I heard a familiar voice. It was the professor from Nottingham holding forth on the German Democratic Republic and telling of its impending collapse. Within minutes of my arrival, he had ended his oration and was under attack from any number of the audience for his 'cold war warrior attitudes'. An East German professor of sociology, an SED member, got up to deliver the *coup de grâce*. 'I do not know which country the speaker is referring to but it certainly isn't mine.' His contribution was met with a storm of applause from a section of the audience. I ought to have good prospects of recruiting someone from that constituency I thought. Not having expected to see my Nottingham acquaintance in Long

Beach, California, I left the conference centre as unobtrusively as possible, so that I had some time to think out the situation.

I had been sent on 'holiday' to the Long Beach conference, which had attracted hundreds of American scholars in the German studies field, and a considerable minority of West Germans. The German Democratic Republic was represented by just three or four 'travel cadres', those the Party thought could be allowed out and who were duty bound to put the SED line. Mine was a late invitation from my political bosses because a colleague, who was announced as going, was sick. At least my name was not on the guest list. I did notice on the guest speakers' list Professor Eva Manske from Leipzig, whom I had met once. She was unlikely to remember. My mission was to evaluate the work and views of Americans on our Republic, make contacts, exercise influence and, if possible, make a recruit for the Stasi. From past experience we knew the British did not attend, usually on grounds of cost. My Nottingham man had proved to be an exception. Of course, there was always a chance we would not meet in such a large assembly. Even if we did, I had my usual cover, that of literary editor; there was nothing wrong with that. Still, I felt less free with his presence, considering what I had revealed to him in Leipzig only a year before. If we met and he chose to mention my English origins it would be very embarrassing, particularly if any of my Party comrades were present. I must keep a low profile and attend lectures and working parties he was unlikely to.

That evening we had an official dinner at the Hyatt Edgewater Hotel where many of us were staying. I crept in and, as most of the tables were full, chose a space near the door, without looking too closely with whom I was going to be sitting. I believed I could see my Nottingham 'friend' right at the other end of the vast dining suite. After establishing that there was a free seat, I sat down at the half empty table for eight. On my right was an assistant professor from Troy State University, European Campus, while on my left the seat remained empty except for a copy of *Newsweek*. I looked around the table; I was clearly the oldest of the five present. I asked myself what the hell I was doing there. Then I thought, 'Well, you've never been to southern California before, and you probably won't come again. Blow it, just enjoy the ride and forget the politics.'

On knowing I was from East Berlin, my American neighbour immediately started asking what I thought about that guy from Notting…ham' with apparently huge emphasis on the 'ham'. Suffering from considerable jet lag and age lag, at 63, I just did not want to talk politics. I replied simply that certainly some of his criticisms were true and some of us were aware of our shortcomings. But, of course, there was no chance of the Republic collapsing, and certainly no prospect of German re-unification. As I attempted to finish my soup, he persisted in going on about Honecker's plan to turn our Republic into one of the world leaders in micro-chip production. What nonsense I thought, we're using stolen IBM designs, but I just enjoyed my asparagus soup. Suddenly, the Trojan stopped. I looked up and followed his gaze. He was trying to attract the attention of a most striking, tall, slender, black woman, who had entered through the far door of the suite. Oh God! Who could say the slogan, 'Black is beautiful' was not true! I watched her progress among and along the tables. As she got nearer, I took in her appearance more clearly. She had what I can only describe as a noble head and features. She was dressed in a long eight-buttoned buttermilk, double-breasted, summer jacket, blue jeans and high heels. She wore long, gold earrings and a light gold chain around her neck. 'Marlene, over here,' the Trojan called. I could not believe it as she got nearer, and nearer to our table. I was almost breathless as she sat down next to me. My Troy colleague asked if she had been successful. She said she had not but would, perhaps, try again later.

'By the way, Marlene, this is Professor ... er'. I stepped in quickly, 'I'm not a professor just a kind of editor. Just call me Martin.'

'Hi, pleased to meet you, Martin,' she responded with an enthusiastic smile which highlighted her amazing teeth but also her wonderful cheek bones. She explained she had been attempting to phone her sister who lived in the area but had failed. She had flown in from Washington DC.

I'm sure my neighbour from Troy regarded me as very impolite. I had not meant to be, but, I did not want to be serious, the local wine had a soothing effect, I felt relaxed and I just allowed the waves of Marlene's charm to simply sweep over me. At one point, I was awakened from my reverie by our kind preacher-like host, Professor Christian Soe, originally from Denmark and indeed a Lutheran pastor's son. I nearly greeted him in Danish and then I thought better of it. After all, the only Danes I had known were members of the Waffen-SS, most of them dead long ago. After his polite enquiry whether everything was OK, I quickly got back to my previous state. Had anyone asked me later, I'm sure I could not have repeated one sentence spoken by Dr Klaus Ruppecht, Deputy Consul General of the Federal Republic of Germany, Los Angeles, who was our after dinner guest speaker.

After dinner I invited Marlene for a drink which she gracefully accepted. Either to impress me that she was a serious researcher or out of genuine interest - I do not know which - she did ask some highly relevant questions about the Republic I had served since 1949. I admitted to her any number of reforms could have been initiated without, in my view, endangering the system. She hoped I did not mind her saying that she thought most of what appeared in *Neues Deutschland* was a 'load of crap'. I said did not and told her an anti-*Neues Deutschland* joke. We broke up towards midnight and found we were on the same floor. As we had gone up in the lift I had been in two minds over a question, but standing in front of her door, it simply came out, 'I hope I didn't bore you too much with my…'

'Oh, of course, not Martin. It's been a blast,' she interjected.

'Great. I'd like to be able to spend some more time with you tomorrow, …if you don't have any other plans,' I added hesitantly. To my relief, she said she was definitely going to the session on 'Transatlantic Perceptions of Germans and Americans: The Role of Journalists and Publicists'. I said I'd see her there and with that she gave me a kiss on the cheek which was reciprocated and she disappeared into her room. Later, I realised Eva Manske from Leipzig would be one of the speakers, but no longer cared. I fell asleep with thoughts and images of Marlene swirling round my head. And with the help of the Californian wine we'd been drinking, I had one of the best night's sleep I'd had in years.

I arrived late for the morning session and I noticed Marlene near the front with a white American male of about her own age, 35 or so. My hopes were dashed. I consoled myself that at least the Nottingham 'cold war warrior' was not present. After the meeting I was leaving when I heard my name called.

'Hi, Martin.' It was her. My heart rate quickened and my senses sharpened.

'Ah Marlene, I thought you were occupied, I did not want to disturb you.'

She ignored my remarks and asked simply, 'Going for lunch?'

'Yes, that would be nice,' I replied. Over our meal she asked a great many questions both political and personal

ke, 'Are you married?' 'Do you have children?' Her
irectness was both refreshing and disarming. I told her a
ttle of my two losses. She reached out her hand in
ympathy putting it on mine. What a great sensation! After
unch we skipped the final session and went to see a
rilliant exhibition of cartoons from the famous German
atirical magazine, *Simplicissimus*. Although I had no
esigns on Marlene, I could not help being shocked and
iade to feel a bit foolish by one cartoon which depicted a
oung woman, who was being married off, more for
easons of economics than anything else, to an old man,
He'll make a good husband, he's a bit sickly already,' was
ie caption. We had supper together and, as I escorted her
> her door, we both said, more or less simultaneously that
e were at a lose end now the conference had ended. She
earched my eyes. We agreed to meet next morning for
reakfast at ten in the hotel breakfast room. The conference
'as over. I had conducted no propaganda, made no
onverts and recruited no one. I was a complete and utter
op, but I didn't give a damn.

found Marlene at 10.10 eating a weight watchers'
reakfast. Mercifully, she was alone. Most of the
onference participants appeared to have already left. I
dered a full American breakfast, something I only ever
id in hotels. It was phenomenal. It reminded me slightly
' my childhood. We talked about ourselves. She told me
ie had been born into the black bourgeoisie in Baltimore.
er father had a chain of shops. He had spoilt her rotten.
fter Johns Hopkins University, she had continued her

studies in Paris and Munich. The demands of a fairly humble job in the State Department had been a factor in the breakdown of her marriage, after which, she had turned to the academic life. We talked on about this and that, the conference, the hotel, our colleagues, but we both knew we wanted to talk about other things. She said she would like to visit San Diego which was supposed to be beautiful and where she had never been. I said I had never been there either. In that case, why didn't I join her? I was momentarily stunned and then said, 'Yes, please.' She had a hire car, a large Ford, which she told me, she had not ordered. 'They gave me an upgrade at no extra cost.' It was one of the new range of American cars designed to defeat the Japanese onslaught with plenty of leg room, air conditioning, sun roof, electric windows, automatic transmission, power steering, an almost noiseless engine, the latest audio system, central locking, a massive boot and much, much more. What a change from my old Wartburg! An hour later, we were on our way south along the coast highway. Nina Simone was singing, 'Be my husband' on the car radio. Marlene's white loosely fitting silk and linen dress contrasted delightfully with her dark skin and fitted loosely around the curves of her body. Wow! What a lucky old bastard I was, I thought. I mused and considered that two weeks previously as I had sat at my desk in the Stasi complex in Normannen Strasse, Berlin, Lichtenberg, I had no idea that any of this was going to happen to me. For once, I said to myself, 'Thank you, Comrade General Erich Mielke! Thank you very much! And thank you Professor Soe!'

Half way there we stopped for coffee and changed drivers. I drove a little unsteadily at first as I had never driven such a large vehicle before, let alone in America and on the congested 405 Interstate highway. I talked at random, the way you do when you are excited by the company. I remarked, 'I hope I can get a small souvenir of this, for me, wonderful, introduction to your country.' Marlene, in a quick manoeuvre, had her knickers off and waved them at me, 'Here' she cried, 'will they do?' She pushed them into the pocket of my linen jacket. What could I say? It would've been rude not to accept.

For a moment, I saw Comrade Mielke's stern face warning me about the dangers of women and the way the CIA would not hesitate to use them. He had once brought this theme into a lecture at the Stasi's own university in Potsdam. I remember how he paused and, straight-faced, looked round the room when he had finished giving us details of a particularly, salacious case. I thought then and I thought now, 'Yes, and what have we done?' But I had to consider the question, 'Was Marlene a CIA plant? Why should such a beautiful and talented woman waste her time with an old guy like me?' Had she really got the car to impress me? 'You too can have one of these if you join us?' I heard echoing in my head. I looked desperately for evidence the other way. Firstly, it was unlikely the CIA were on to me. Secondly, the CIA would not risk it with a black woman, because they could not be sure that black flesh would be to my taste. I had never longed to be with a

227

black woman or, for that matter, with a woman of a particular nationality. It appeared my tastes were catholic!

We stopped at the tourist information centre at La Jolla on the outskirts of San Diego to enquire about hotels. The Bay Club Hotel Marina by the waterfront had a special offer on and looked splendid so we chose that. On arrival, I parked the car. It looked great. I asked her cautiously whether it was two rooms or one we were going for.

'Oh Martin, Martin,' she said in mock impatience, 'When are you going to stop fucking me about and go to bed with me?' The penny had finally dropped; even I got the message. It was a beautiful room overlooking the water. We discovered we were both novices in inter-ethnic bridge-building. It was a beautiful experience.

Marlene knew what she wanted and knew how to get it and she got it several times during the next three days. She rode me majestically and confidently. What a wonderful sight! She also introduced me to the pleasures of a Jacuzzi for two with champagne; something I never imagined could be so exciting. I had enjoyed my sexual partners in the past, but I realised I had not met anyone quite like her since Hilde. How different and yet how similar they were. How exciting an attractive, educated, independent woman was!

We visited the La Jolla Museum of Contemporary Art and the magnificent Balbao Park, the Quail Botanical Garden and (for me) the stunning shops. I bought Marlene eplacement for 'my souvenir'. She bought me a shirt and ny first pair of jeans – a pair of Levi's. I had refused to wear such trousers in Germany. Our Party, Comrade Honecker, had spent years denouncing them as part of the US cultural imperialism, but in recent times jeans had become almost a 'must' among the trendy intellectuals of the SED and the Stasi. As it was Marlene who was asking me to wear them, I thought, 'To hell with it, I'll join the crowd.'

We went over the frontier into Mexico to Tijuana. What a contrast! Although the frontier town was clearly benefiting from proximity to the US, there was a surprising amount of poverty. Where were all the oil revenues going I wondered? 'To Switzerland', answered the young man in the gift shop. It had not helped, he went on, having the same party in power for, how long was it, seventy years? I knew exactly what he meant.

Like all good things our three days came to an end no sooner than they had begun. We tried to be cheerful on the long drive to LA airport. Marlene became quite emotional and cried. I had not really expected that from such an apparently strong woman. She said that I should stop running myself down and stop worrying about my age. I said I felt great, particularly having met her, but could not deny my birth certificate. I tried to explain to her how difficult it was for a citizen of the German Democratic Republic to remain friends with a Westerner. But I promised I would attempt to keep in touch. She promised to attempt to visit Berlin. I momentarily thought of defection. The CIA would welcome me with open arms, but their 'debriefing' would be quite an ordeal. Through my reading over the years, through American movies, music and fashion, I had come to realise that there was much to admire in America. For me, it had started with Paul Robeson, John Garfield, Henry Fonda, Upton Sinclair and Ernest Hemingway. However, it was a country which was full of contradictions. I could not stay; I was not the defecting type and I still hoped for better things in the Socialist Camp. Sadly, I boarded the big Boeing 747 jet for Frankfurt International airport. As the aircraft gathered speed for take-off, images of my last few days flashed through my mind, a tear came to my eye and I hoped this was not the last I would see of America or of Marlene.

32.

November Days 1989

I was glad I did not have to go my Normannen Strasse office on 15 January 1990. On that day, the People's Police unit guarding the Stasi building was forced to yield to The People, a large assembly of 100,000, who were determined to gain unauthorised entry and who had been organised by the opposition group, New Forum. Few of my colleagues were in the building; our Ministry was already into a state of disintegration and dismemberment by that time. Manfred Sauer, the government advisor, told Parliament earlier on that very day that the Stasi had had 85,000 regular employees, but that 30,000 had already been dismissed. Quite breathtaking was the admission that our Ministry had 109,000 secret informers, that is, almost 1 for every 80 people in the country. This was far more than Himmler's Gestapo. Few of us had any idea that Mielke had built up such a vast internal spy network. We were never given details. The crowd which stormed the Stasi HQ did little damage in material terms, but far more in psychological terms. One other aspect of the storming was that some files went 'missing'. Had Mielke got his men among the crowd? It seemed likely.

There were few, if any, of us in the Ministry who were not shaken-up by the rapid succession of events from September 1989 onwards. The ever increasing demonstrations had begun in the summer; first in Berlin Leipzig and Dresden, and then in virtually all the towns of the Republic. It certainly was a domino effect. These were naturally very intimidating in a state where there had been nothing like it since the suppressed revolt of June 1953 Gorbachev's visit to 'celebrate' forty years of the Republic in October was virtually a death sentence in that he made it clear he would not sanction the use of Soviet forces to stop the people from realising their demands. The demands were simple, they were for freedom to organise, free access to the media, and freedom to travel. Many thousands of our citizens were voting with their feet and leaving the Republic via Czechoslovakia and Hungary into Austria. It was hoped that the palace coup against Honecker, on 1st October, would restore stability. But his successor, Egon Krenz, failed totally. On 4 November, our former boss Markus Wolf, openly sided with the masses. He was one of the speakers at a mammoth demonstration of 500,000 in Berlin on Alexanderplatz called by the theatrical trade union. Berlin had probably never seen anything like this before. The entire government resigned on 7 November and the following day the Politburo gave up. I must admit was not sorry to see the back of Mielke and his subsequent arrest for misuse of office. Hans Modrow, a reformer from Dresden, whom I knew slightly from our days in Soviet captivity, took over the government on 13 November, and General Wolfgang Schwanitz became the new head of the Stasi. For a brief period we had hope that genuine reforms would come, that reliable leaders, like Wolf, would keep a tight grip to stop the reform movement from getting out of hand. This proved to be a complete illusion. Once the frontiers of the Republic, including the Berlin Wall, were thrown open on 9 November, there was no way that the old order could be preserved.

On that November night of unreserved, hysterical joy on the streets of Berlin and elsewhere in the Republic, I walked along the Unter den Linden in the direction of the Brandenburg Gate and watched the crowds swarm towards the Wall and through it. Others were actually on it having used sledge hammers to help knock bits down. It was unbelievable! There was a dream-like atmosphere, an air of total disbelief and unreality. What was so surprising was that it was all so good-natured. After some hesitation, I joined the surge forward towards the West. There was little the frontier police could do to control the crowds. Some stood there smiling, some looked perplexed, others thoughtful, one or two a little fearful. Most of the arrogance and swagger of only a few days before had vanished, and so had their authority. By the time I neared the control point they had given up attempting to issue exit visas. We just flowed through. Joyful crowds awaited us on the other side. A woman stepped forward and hugged and kissed me. Other West Berliners were doing the same to other East Berliners as they came through. Here and there were youths with sparklers. There were those who sang, and those who danced while others stood there sobbing. Some were searching anxiously for friends and relatives. One person was offering free *Sekt* to the East German 'visitors', another offered flowers, a third chocolates. Even East German frontier police were offered gifts; embarrassed, they took them. They had never expected 'the class enemy' to 'fight' them like this. West Berlin police were standing around and just smiling or reporting back the unfolding spectacle on their radios to headquarters. Western television and radio teams were already on the scene relaying the drama to the outside world. As I and others swept westwards along the Avenue 17 Juni, curious and excited West Berliners and foreign tourists moved in the opposite direction. Cars, mopeds and bicycles sounded their hooters and bells. I suddenly realised I had no West German money, but I need not have bothered. Bus drivers were not collecting fares from East Germans while some bars were dispensing free drinks. There was a festive air on the streets of West Berlin; something unique in my life was happening.

I arrived back in my flat about 8 a.m. and was just about to take a shower when the phone rang. It was Marlene ringing from Washington DC. She was very enthusiastic and excited about the events of the night before and had decided to drop everything and come to Berlin if that was O.K.? What could I say? In the six months or so since we ad met at the conference she had phoned me four times nd had written several times. I had responded with erhaps three cards and two letters. What would I tell her? As far as she was concerned I was just another minor iterary editor and a nice guy. What would she think when he discovered I was an agent of the detested regime which ad built and kept that damned Wall in place? I dreaded to hink.

ater that morning I arrived in the office where things were appening at pace. We received a signal. We had to be eady to destroy sensitive files. At the same time, iscussions were advanced to separate our service from the est of the Ministry for State Security. We would be a ompletely independent external intelligence service. It vas a great relief to hear this. However, the mood was bad, norale was poor. News was coming in of one or two uicides, of nervous breakdowns and of defections to the Vest German Federal Intelligence Service (BND). There vas talk of betrayal by our political masters and by the oviets. I went home tired after a long day. I nearly fell sleep in the underground but was nudged awake by the ostling crowds on their way west. I did fall asleep in front f the television, shortly after my arrival at the flat. I was woken by the telephone. Another crisis, I thought. Or was t Marlene, she could not come after all? It was my 17-ear-old son, Heine, ringing very excitedly from Hamburg. here were thousands of East Germans there. The rostitutes of St Pauli were offering their services at half rice to East Germans! He just wanted to know his father

was all right and ask whether I'd been to the West yet. He
was glad to hear that I had.

Marlene had no difficulty in getting a visa or a very
reasonable deal at the Palast Hotel. She somehow managed
to get a flight to Berlin through a connection of hers in Pan
Am's Washington office. She was that kind of person. I
awaited her at Tegel, West Berlin's airport, on the
following Saturday, 11 November. Only a few days before
it would have been well-nigh impossible for me to do that.
How quickly things were changing.

Despite jet lag, Marlene looked as beautiful as ever and
when we hugged smelt delightful. People turned and
looked at us, this 63-year-old East German literary-type
with the hint of a soldier about him, with this stunning
black woman with a hint of 'class' about her, who was
obviously very much younger. I was glad to see her, proud
to be seen with her, but I was a little awkward at first. She
attempted to put me at my ease by talking non-stop. We
travelled by *S-Bahn*, the metropolitan train, to
Alexanderplatz, and then by taxi to her hotel. I had not
been in the lobby of the Palast since my aborted meeting
with 'Diana'. I hoped there would be a different
receptionist. Just my luck it was the same 30-something
person. What were the odds? Hell, what was I worried
about. It was nearly three years ago! He did not seem to
recognise me. We went to her tastefully decorated room
where she expected, and got, some real kissing, hugging
and fondling. She was lovely. How lucky I was, but I felt

236

erk. I was nearly twice her age, a Stasi schmuck and an ex-SS soldier living in a different world. Or was I? I stopped short of the sex act. I feigned another meeting but agreed to have supper that evening.

I took her to the Ganymed just off Friedrich Strasse. For once, it was almost empty. The action was elsewhere. We skated round all the topics we had in common. She expressed the view that she thought the German Democratic Republic was finished. What did I think? I took a more cautious view but agreed she could be right. She was anxious to see my 'space' as she put it, and so after supper we walked along the canal bank to Friedrich Strasse and took the underground. The stations were crowded, even more than usual for a Saturday night.

As we approached my concrete block of flats, I warned her not to expect much despite the street's big name, Leninallee. My place was just that of a poor East German widower. In fact, I felt poorer still when I heard that our East mark was exchanging for 10 (West) D-mark. She thought my flat was small but 'charming'. I thought of the bathrooms in the Hyatt in Long Beach, Bay Club Hotel in San Diego, the Palast, and looked at mine. It was a dump! We had a bottle of Californian wine she had brought and watched more scenes of euphoria on television; the roads to the West jammed with our pathetic Trabants, the never ending crowds going to West Berlin, Chancellor Kohl and ex-Chancellor Willy Brandt speaking in West Berlin to enthusiastic crowds, the continuing demonstrations in

Leipzig and elsewhere. Thankfully, there was no violence anywhere.

As midnight approached I mentioned to Marlene that perhaps she should be getting back to her hotel. She reacted rather hurt, saying she was not Cinderella. pointed out it was illegal for her to spend the night elsewhere. Did I want her to go, she asked. Had I met another woman in the meantime? I reassured her on both counts and she said, 'Well then Martin, if it's all the same to you I'm going to stay.'

Fuck the SED! Fuck the Stasi! I thought to myself, 'OK fuck them! Fantastic!' I shouted out. I did not resist. I was one of the luckiest men alive, and certainly even luckier relative to my age group. I opened a good bottle of Champagne I had been saving and just relaxed. I let her lead the way. I was not to be disappointed and from her reaction neither was she.

On Sunday 12 November, the Berlin Philharmonic Orchestra hastily organised a solidarity concert for East Germans in the Cultural Forum on Kemperplatz in West Berlin. Daniel Barenboim conducted. We decided to go. An audience of over 2,000 heard Beethoven's Concerto for Piano and Orchestra and his 7th Symphony. In the 1940s, had first heard the 7th in some film with Henry Fonda. It had moved me then. It hit me hard now. It was as if my entire life was sweeping before me. I could not hold back the tears. As we left I tried to get a grip on myself. As we walked through the *Tiergarten*, I told her I needed to tell

…er some things about myself. I hoped when we had finished our walk she would still want to go on seeing me.

…explained that this was the reason why I had suggested she go back to her hotel on the previous evening. She immediately thought I'd been telling lies and had a wife or another long-term relationship. Having eliminated those possibilities she was greatly relieved. I started at the beginning, or nearly so. I told her about the SS, Moscow, the People's Police and the HVA. She listened transfixed. 'So you're a spy?' she asked rhetorically. I said, 'I prefer to say, I'm a professional intelligence officer. All states have them, even Sweden and Switzerland. I have hardly ever spied anywhere. I have largely analysed reports in East Berlin.'

'Were you spying when we met?'

'If you want to put it in those terms, I must answer in the affirmative.' I admitted somewhat reluctantly.

'Well that's just wonderful,' she said sarcastically.

'Marlene, I did not know I was going to meet you. It was all so unexpected. What was I supposed to say? For all I knew you could have been CIA. Don't tell me you don't think there wasn't a CIA agent or contact there. I'm sure there was. Even telling you now, I'm breaking all the rules, even being here in West Berlin, I'm breaking the rules.'

We reached the *Gedächtniskirche* (Memorial Church) and found a table in a nearby Croat restaurant. As we sat there in silence, she suddenly blurted out, 'And what about your SS days? How many people did you kill then?'

'Frankly, I do not know. I never, never, shot people who didn't have a gun in their hands. It was a case of my life or theirs.'

'Do you swear that?' she asked purposefully.

'Yes, I do! And what's more, you, and I too, would give some kid brought up in the Chicago ghetto, who got into crime, a second chance. Well, what about my generation here? Many of us got the Nazi ideology at home, we got it at school, we got it at the movies and we got it from the Nazis themselves. We got it everywhere we turned. Some even got it from people like Henry Ford. No one put the alternative story to us.'

She looked quizzically, 'What do you mean, Ford?'

'I mean quite simply that he spent millions of dollars to pour out anti-Semitic poison world-wide. It was mentioned at the Nuremberg Trials. The Americans did not like to hear it.'

'I did not know that... I bet they didn't.' she said thoughtfully.

As we walked towards the *Zoo* train station we were hand in-hand once again, although there was much to reflect upon. I insisted that Marlene spent the night in her hotel. 'We've talked a lot and I've really told you a great many unpleasant things about myself. It's best if you go and sleep on it. I'll ring you first thing tomorrow.' I said reluctantly, but knowing it was the best way. She agreed was right.

On Monday, the day Modrow took over the government, was expected at the office. The position of our organisation was getting more precarious day-by-day. Overnight it came to a head. Whether Marlene broke off with me or not, I ought to break free from a system which, in its present form, I no longer approved of. Reports indicated that discipline in the armed forces was weakening. The numbers leaving the Republic for good were showing no signs of slackening, despite the new open frontiers policy. Later, I reached Marlene and she said she would come round to my place in the evening. I bought a few things from our 'company store' for our meal and hoped she would turn up.

Marlene did turn up. All went well. She stayed the night and we enjoyed each other's company and wonderful night's sex. She left the next day just in time to pick up her things from the hotel and catch the *S-Bahn* to Friedrich Strasse, cross the frontier, take another train for Zoo in the West and then the excellent airport bus to Tegel Airport. She was very pleased about my decision to leave the HVA. '...if that's what you really want.' She invited me to visit her in Washington once I had hung my uniform in the cupboard.

I did not take early retirement and I did not visit Marlene. In December 1989, Modrow was forced to close down the new Office for National Security, which was meant to replace the Ministry for State Security. The HVA went too. We were all sent home for good! With Germany still divided I still needed a visa to visit the USA and I was unlikely to get one if the truth about me ever came out.

Rather than cause Marlene any embarrassment I did not apply. By 3 October 1990, Germany was reunited. We were all citizens of one state again. I had half-expected to be arrested. Most of the East German leaders, from Honecker and Mielke down, faced arrest and trial. Markus Wolf and some others from the HVA suffered the same fate. Wolf maintained his cool and had quite a few friends outside Germany. He said quite simply, he was a professional intelligence officer working for an internationally recognised state. He had killed no one, ordered no one to be killed. Eventually, the Constitutional Court worked out a formula which cleared Wolf and others, like me, pronouncing, in effect, that only West Germans who had spied for the East could be prosecuted. It was 1994 before this judgement of Solomon was given. I had had some anxious moments until then. Now, released from that tension, I had only the problem of filling in the long days of idleness, the psychological and intellectual problem of coming to terms with my past for the second time in my life, and the practical problem of living on a small pension.

33.

Heinke, the Woman from the Wall

In the years following Marlene's visit both our lives changed. I did not accept her invitations, for which I was very grateful, even after 3 October 1990. I felt it would have been unfair to her. I had little to offer. I felt terrible. I missed her brains, wit, beauty and joy. If I woke up at night, I invariably started thinking about her and wondering whether I'd been stupid to let her go, wondering how she was. Eventually, she found a fellow academic in Washington and they were married. Happily, we stayed in touch and I am sure we will always have feelings for each other. As for me, I had one of those unusual experiences which have marked my eventful life.

Since Marlene's visit I had haunted the lobby, corridors, bars, and occasionally, the restaurants of the Palast Hotel, even though it was getting too expensive for me. It was the night of the first elections since the restoration of German unity, December 1990. Kohl and his Christian Democrats were set to sweep back into office. I went to the Palast to have a drink and take in the atmosphere. As I sat there watching the results on television, a female voice, whispered, 'Excuse me for talking to you but...you did cross through The Wall on 9 November...Yes?' I looked up and it slowly dawned on me, 'You kissed me!'

She was slightly embarrassed now, 'Yes, I did. It was such an emotional moment. Well, I just wanted to know how you are.'

I offered my new acquaintance a drink. We decided on a bottle of Henkell Trocken, 'the fine classic *Sekt* from the Rhine'. She introduced herself as Heinke Kohl. I could not resist the temptation to say, 'No relation I suppose?'

'Oh no, thank God! I voted against him today. I normally vote FDP, but this time, I voted SPD.'

'Could I ask why?'

She paused, 'Kohl's lot will win anyway and we need a strong opposition. Secondly, I do think Oskar Lafontaine was right to point out the difficulties, as well as the joys, unification would bring.' She looked to me for my reaction. I hesitated for a second. 'Kohl's not all that bad really, but I have to admit, you've given two very good reasons to vote for an opposition party. I voted for them too!'

We talked late into the night getting slightly depressed as Kohl's forecast victory became reality. I realised I had missed talking to an intelligent, independently-minded woman who read. It was so long since I had spoken to a German woman of this type, solid middle class and thinking. They could be very impressive. She read *Die Zeit*, the respected Hamburg weekly, a publication I had only seen intermittently. Divorced, she came from Hamburg where she had her own women's fashion boutique. On the night The Wall opened she had been visiting her son, who was a student at the Free University in West Berlin. That was only her second visit to the divided city. She also had a daughter who was married. She had another day in Berlin and asked if we could meet up before she left, otherwise I could ring her in Hamburg if I ever headed in that direction.

I now had all the time in the world so I rang Heinke later that Monday. We strolled round the restored Nicholai Quarter in East Berlin and then stopped in the Grand Hotel on Friedrich Strasse for a coffee and a slice of their wonderful *Apfeltorte* and cream. Opened in 1987, it had been Honecker's finest. They stung you for everything, but at least you could sit undisturbed for hours in a 'luxurious' setting. We chatted, with Heinke doing most of the talking. Her style was bright, enthusiastic, up-beat. She told me about how she had felt overpowered by her husband, whom she had married young, and how she had decided to strike out on her own. After completing grammar school, she had taken up a course in tourism of which her husband had been the director. He was a masculine, handsome man but rather boring. 'An unthinking Conservative, a Christian Democrat,' she recalled. She had found she had intellectual interests which he did not. She was reading Stahlberg's autobiography, *The Accursed Duty*, about his life as an officer in Hitler's Germany and the campaign in Russia. I confessed I did not know the book, but promised to look it up. I said obliquely, I had been there too. She volunteered the information that she had divorced at 50, five years ago. Later, I said if she had nothing better to do she could go home with me for a meal. She readily agreed.

I had taken the precaution of preparing a few things, 'just in case' and tidied up the flat. The tidying up had not taken long. I am a tidy person by nature and I have not been a great consumer. I am good on bathrooms and had done a thorough job there and in the kitchen ensured nothing unpleasant was lingering in the fridge, but the dusty windows I had ignored. By the time we arrived, the grey day had turned into a cold night. She was very interested in my pictures, rugs and other mementos. After admiring my Russian landscape, she focused on a pint-size, transparent beer mug which, in between two gold bands proclaimed 'Arizona State University'. Had I been to Arizona? I had to explain that I had not, but that a kind Professor Kleinfeldt, had given it me as a souvenir of my visit to a conference in California with the hope that one day I would visit Arizona. The Professor, who was himself from Arizona, had a large moustache and, not withstanding his name, was, if anything, more English than German, but was actually American-born and bred. In self-mockery, I admitted to having been, 'a good boy, who was let out of the German Democratic Republic occasionally'. Almost inevitably, being a prosperous, middle-class, West German, Heinke had been to 'the States' and to both

California and Arizona. I could not hold that against her, could I?

She had insisted on buying two bottles of wine, Baron de Rothschild red from France, and by the time we had finished them and a little of a bottle of Bulgarian I had spare, while listening to my Nina Simone compilation tape that Marlene had brought me, we felt in a mood of goodwill towards all men. 'Oh come on, I don't have to go back,' she beamed straight into my eyes. 'Let's go to bed and see what happens. If nothing happens that's ok, if it does, then great!' I enthusiastically accepted her challenge and, yes, it was great.

A few days after Heinke's departure, I received a copy of Stahlberg's book in the post with the inscription, 'For Martin, with thanks for a wonderful time, yours Heinke.' I started to see Heinke quite regularly. Because of her business I often went to Hamburg rather than her coming to Berlin. It was so easy to take the train. I enjoyed my new life and realised even more how terrible and unnatural the division of Germany had been. My son decided to study economics at Hamburg University and Heinke helped him in various ways. After my second visit, I told her about my past. I commented that I was surprised she had never asked. She said she was curious but she thought I would tell her more about myself when I was ready. I explained to her how I had gone from being a sergeant in the Waffen-SS to being a colonel in the HVA. She said she had thought it was something like that. I had a military bearing and was, what people used to call, 'well-groomed'. She was glad to have been brought up in the West and could not judge those who were not. On the second day of my second visit, I told her it was confession time again, this time positively my last. She was enchanted by the story of my childhood in Guernsey. 'It's even better than the Stahlberg biography. You ought to write about it.' She said encouragingly. She liked me better for my mistakes and better still as an Englishman.

'I thought you looked interesting in the Palast Hotel. I was not totally sure you were the man I had kissed but I thought I would chance it anyway.' Then she added, 'I've got a confession too. I hope you won't despise me.' Her family owned property in East Berlin which was being restored to them. Her brother had it in-hand. She felt guilty that she had done nothing towards it, had not worked to buy the property. But her brother had explained that if they did not get it back then it would simply be sold off to some big property company. In any case, it had been used by one of the mass organisations. They were not dislodging anyone. We both felt more relaxed after our confessions, and the friendship deepened.

34.

Madrid Visit 1996, looking for new shores

I had always wanted to visit Spain which, in emotional terms, had meant a great deal to me. For decades this was impossible. Now the impossible had become possible. As the 60th anniversary of the outbreak of the Civil War approached in 1996, I got increasingly restless. The flights to Spain were cheap, no one could object to me going there, so I booked a package to Madrid staying at the Victoria Hotel overlooking a pleasant square. It was filled with German, Dutch and Spanish tourists. The Germans, included a sizeable group from the former East German Republic who, even more than me, were making up for lost time. Almost inevitably, I thought I saw one of my old Stasi contacts, a fifty-something 'Herr Dr' and his much younger, attractive East European wife. Were they collaborators or were they victims? Were they just faces in an old file? I do not know. If we had ever met, they did not seem to recognise me; they were too absorbed in each other. I was happy for them. It was better not to pursue my curiosity and I held it in check. I was surprised how ignorant both the German and the British tourists were about the Spanish Civil War on this, the 60th anniversary of its outbreak. After all, blood had been spilled on virtually all the streets we walked along.

Three weeks before my departure I had received a letter from my Nottingham professor, who was doing some research on the German part in the Spanish Civil War. We had exchanged a few postcards since 1988 and had not quite met each other in Long Beach. I wrote back and as he had mentioned visiting Madrid suggested that we meet there. We finally came face to face, again in one of those symbols of modern Spain, the restaurant of *El Corte Ingles* department store just off the Plaza del Sol. After a snack we took the metro to Ciudad Universitaria, the scene of heavy fighting in 1936. As we walked about Madrid, drank coffee, beer and wine, I told him most of my story. He said he had suspected some of what I told him, but was still quite taken aback by the rest. We toured the military museum together and were shocked that it was still totally Francoist in its account of the Civil War, and this, twenty years after Spain had become a democracy. We spent nearly a day together in Queen Sophia's Museum of Modem Art where the famous Picasso painting *Guernica* attracts large numbers of the faithful, the curious and even some detractors. Though my head was in favour of the work, it did not arouse me emotionally. I found Pablo Gargallo's *Great Prophet* (1933), a sculpture in bronze far more powerful and disturbing. There was also a painting of a public execution by garrotting in 1895, which for me was far more compelling that Picasso's masterpiece.

I had tried to keep up with events in Britain through my reading, but it is always more satisfying to hear about developments from a native.

'Are there still so many foreigners in London?' I asked.

'Yes, but now more Japanese and Chinese than in the 1960s,' the professor answered factually.

'Is it true that there are so many beggars everywhere now?'

'Yes, I'm afraid so; in all major towns and cities now, unlike in your day. London has been trying to catch up with Madrid on this one, but I think Madrid still has a few more.' The professor threw me a sardonic smile.

'Does the great Harrods' sale still attract so many people?'

'I am sure it does, but Harrods is now Arab-owned and you have to pay to go to the lavatory there,' he admitted with some annoyance.

'Is the monarchy still as popular as ever?' I enquired.

'Not according to the public opinion polls but they seem to carry on regardless.'

And so I went on exhausting the poor man. I attempted to bring my interrogation to a close, 'Any other changes I should be aware of?'

He thought for a minute, 'Well, the English Sunday has completely disappeared. It's given way to consumerism and big business. Many of the police are likely to be armed, and most of the milkmen have been made redundant.'

'Whaw, the old country has changed,' I concluded with a laugh.

On our last day, I waited for him in the early evening in a restaurant on the Plaza Mayor. Usually very punctual, he was a little late this time. I contemplated my life as I waited. How different it all could have been. If I had not been persuaded by John Amery to join the Waffen-SS where would life have taken me? Probably, I would have slipped back into the old ways. From all accounts, I would have been pressurised to do so. Probably, I would have embarked upon to a career in a bank in Guernsey! From all that I have read about the development of the Channel Islands as havens for British people seeking to avoid tax, I have to presume this would have been my most likely career. If not banking, perhaps I would have taken up a career in tourism. I would have married a girl like Dorothy and missed, Hilde, Galina, Alex, Helga, Julia, Pari, Marlene and the others. Certainly, I would have seen less, experienced less and learned less about the world had I not made that ghastly mistake. In some respects, I have been very, very lucky. I regret my mistakes; I do not regret my life. I've tried to live a moral life despite the 'slings and arrows of outrageous fortune.' I have not got beyond Shakespeare in thinking that life is 'a tale full of sound and fury, yet, signifying nothing.' But I have taken up the challenge Shakespeare threw down by those words and attempted to make some sense of life.

The Professor finally arrived just in time to stop me getting maudlin. As the Professor was a refugee from the 'Great British Beef Scare,' we ordered two large Argentine steaks with all the trimmings and a good bottle of Rioja. He inevitably asked about my views on the future, whether I still had hope, how I could keep going given the terrible things I had seen, and the bitter disappointments and betrayals I had suffered. I told him about Kurt Goldstein. He was from a wealthy Jewish family. Like me he had lost his father in the war, though, in his case the 1914-18 war. He had witnessed the fall of the Weimar Republic. He had fought in the International Brigades in Spain. After the collapse there, he had suffered internment in France and then was handed over to the Gestapo by the Vichy French. Goldstein had narrowly missed being gassed in Auschwitz. Force marched to Buchenwald, he was one of the lucky ones and had narrowly escaped death there too. Liberated by the Americans, he remained a Communist and had lived and worked in East Berlin until the collapse there. Even now, in 1996, and well over 80 years-of-age, he was still actively engaged in political and historical discussions. For me, he was something of a model. One had to say 'yes' to life, one had to be optimistic.

The Professor asked me about my ideals. I had to admit, quoting Omar Khayyam, '...the idols I have loved so long have done my credit in men's eye much wrong, have drowned my honour in a shallow cup, and sold my reputation for a song.'

Nevertheless, I assured him that I was still a Socialist. Just because of the Spanish Inquisition did that mean that the message of Jesus - the working class Jew - was invalid? I believed I could endorse the Sermon on the Mount, which was entirely compatible with Socialism. Just because the Nazis misused the idealism of youth by proclaiming a united Europe, did that mean the idea of a united Europe was wrong? I thought not, I told him. To prevent war and promote and maintain democratic values a united Europe was more important than ever.

'And who can say that it is right that the most basic elements of life, water and fuel, should be in private hands and be subject to the gambling and speculation on the stock exchange as our free market politicians want? And at a time when doctors can do so much, who can argue morally that a special operation should be dependent on one's ability to pay? No money, no operation!' I argued. 'Do you think it right that the merchants of death, arms manufacturers, should profit from their trade?' I knew the Professor did not and he was polite enough not to bring up the Soviet Union's activities in this direction. 'And just because Stalin and his imitators were wrong, who can deny that Marx was right in saying that capitalism reduces everything, including the skills of the doctor and the professor, to the nexus of money?' And was Marx wrong when he said capitalism could not solve the contradiction between increasing productivity and our inability to consume what was produced? Under capitalism this mean increasing unemployment.

'My dear friend, we must go on searching for something better. There has to be a better way, otherwise we'll descend into barbarism. You are polite, you have not accused me. I must do that myself. As our Politburo member Horst Sindermann put it, 'We were no heroes.' Yes, we ought to have done more, taken a stand, perhaps have been braver.' I believed we were going to part as friends. He promised he would look up Goldstein in Berlin.

The light was fading over the Plaza Mayor as we finished our bottle of wine. By the way, asked the Professor, 'Whatever happened to Verena, if that's her real name?'

'To be honest, I do not know, but I do not think she has been found out so far, and with so many documents destroyed, I don't think she will be... And before you ask, Hilde.., I never discovered what happened to her. I imagine she died on the retreat from Konigsberg. Millions of Germans remain unaccounted for. As for 'Diana', I cannot disclose her identity. Perhaps she was foolish, but I don't think she did much harm.'

'And Kurt,' the courteous Professor enquired,

'Oh Kurt, he's fine. Kurt went to Israel and continued to work for international brotherhood. In this case, between Jew and Arab.'

In the background the old tape of Paco de Lucia had given way to a newer tape of The Communards pleading, *Don't leave me this way*. I took out a postcard depicting Picasso's painting of a bunch of flowers and two hands one giving, one receiving the flowers in friendship. I asked my friend from Nottingham to sign my brief message to Marlene, who had heard him speak in Long Beach. He did so. My card to Heinke, I had posted the day before. For no apparent reason, the phrase, 'It won't be long now!', came into my head.